Partial
Differentiation

PRENTICE-HALL MATHEMATICS SERIES

ALBERT A. BENNETT, EDITOR

H. A. THURSTON

Associate Professor, Department of Mathematics
University of British Columbia

Partial
Differentiation

Englewood Cliffs, N. J. / 1961
PRENTICE-HALL, INC.

Library of Congress Catalog Card Number: 61-15665

Printed in the United States of America.

65022–C

Preface

Partial differentiation is notoriously a difficult subject. This is somewhat in the nature of a paradox, because the technique of partial differentiation is the same as that of ordinary differentiation: the additional variables are indeed present, but are treated as constants.

The subject can be greatly clarified by an extensive explanation in a textbook covering the whole of calculus. More important is the use of a more logical notation for partial derivatives than is common. A suitable notation exists and has been used by Landau. It is in line with the tendency in calculus to use the notation $f(x)$ and $f'(x)$ rather than y and dx/dy, at least for the theoretical passages. It goes with a clear distinction between function and variable: if f is a function and $y = f(x)$ then y is a variable dependent on x; f' denotes the derivative of f, and dy/dx denotes the derivative of y with respect to x. Further remarks of the superiority of Landau's notation over the familiar one occupy a preliminary chapter.

The familiar notation which is condemned is the use of f_x and f_y for the partial derivatives of the function f. Landau uses f_1 and f_2. There is another notation: $\partial u/\partial x$ or u_x if $u = f(x, y)$. This can be criticized on theoretical and logical grounds, especially if carelessly used; and the natural usage is logically careless. But it has the advantage of brevity and a further advantage in applications. A physicist is happier if pressure is denoted by p than if he has to use some such formula as $\phi(v, t)$. Geometrical and physical intuition thrive better if each physical variable has its symbol. My viewpoint is to consider this notation as merely a convenient abbreviation to be replaced by the longer notation in any case of doubt. Because it is so common, I use it, but try to give a warning each time it might lead to ambiguity.

Ground covered

In this subject, maxima and minima (including second-order-derivative tests), directional derivatives, change-of-variable techniques, and inter-dependent-variable problems are practically compulsory. Differentials are useful and simple enough to understand once one has grasped the fact that $dy:dx$ and D_xy are to one another as a ratio is to a quotient; Taylor's theorem is also useful. There is little about integration, which is really a separate subject, and only enough about partial differential equations to show what solving such an equation means. A full treatment would include most of applied mathematics.

The amount of each "compulsory" part of the subject covered is standard, except that in "maxima and minima" I have omitted LaGrange's multipliers (because their use is only a technique, and good treatments are easy to find), and in "interdependent variables" I have covered the gas-laws in some detail. They are a particularly good model for the theory, and good treatments are not easy to find.

Some of the more difficult proofs of theorems (though not statements of the conditions under which the theorems hold) are postponed to Chapter M, which together with Chapters N, O, and P, contains the underlying theory.

Prerequisites

These are, roughly, what is to be found in any textbook or course of calculus before the start of partial differentiation. The partial Taylor's Theorem rests on the ordinary Taylor's theorem. The remarks on integration rest on ordinary integration. Chapter M is based on limits, continuity, and the mean-value theorem for derivatives.

The reader is expected to know enough analytical geometry to be able to follow geometrical applications and illustrations. Although three-dimensional graphs are explained, this explanation does not pretend to cover the subject in enough detail for the average pupil to understand it.

Units

In this book, letters are used to denote pure numbers: e.g., "let the mass of the body be m gm," m denoting a number, rather than "let the mass be m," m denoting a mass. When a coordinate system is introduced, however, we normally regard the linear unit as implicit: the area of the square whose vertices are (0,0), (0,1), (1,0), and (1,1) is 1, rather than 1 cm² or 1 square coordinate unit. The metric system is used throughout the book.

Acknowledgments

There remains the pleasant duty of acknowledging *coram publico* the help and interest of Dr. Ben Noble and Dr. Tom Flett, who have read the typescript and made many helpful suggestions. Dr. Flett in particular has made many more cogent, constructive, and detailed suggestions than one has a right to expect when asking a friend or colleague to criticize a book, and I have benefited greatly from his advice. The form in which the fundamental theorem of the subject (the proof of the chain-rule) finally appears is his. Because the author has the last word, and there are inevitably places where I have obstinately held to my own point of view, I alone am responsible for any remaining inaccuracies or infelicities.

H. A. THURSTON

Vancouver, B. C.

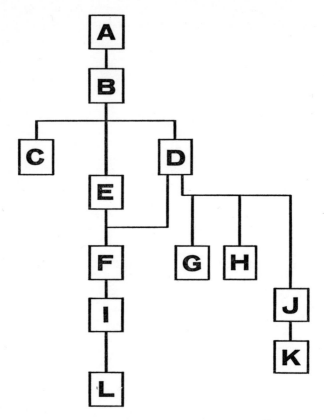

Logical dependence of the chapters in Part I.

[Chapter **K** (maxima and minima) may be read directly after Chapter **B** (basic definitions), if the second-order-derivative test is not required, or if its proof is taken for granted.]

[Chapter **L** (differential equations) may be read directly after Chapter **D** (the chain rule), if only derivatives, not differentials, are to be used.]

Contents

Partial
Differentiation

Introduction

This chapter is intended for students who, having already met partial derivatives, propose to use this book to learn more or to clarify what they have learnt, and for teachers wondering whether the book suits their purposes. It explains why I use certain hitherto uncommon methods and notations. The reader to whom the subject is new is advised not to read this chapter, at least not until he has finished the book.

Part of the difficulty of partial differentiation lies in the mere extra complication of having more than one variable (a typical instance being the long calculation for transforming a second-order derivative from cartesian form into polar form) and becomes less with practice. But a more serious difficulty remains. Many students, even good ones, never become confident in the subject (and some who are, turn out on examination to be falsely so); others, though competent in the technique, are not clear just what the technique is being used for.

When in doubt about a mathematical concept, we can and should appeal to its definition. The partial derivative of $f(x, y)$ with respect to x is often described as the rate-of-change of $f(x, y)$ with x while y remains constant. This is a description rather than a definition, and we should be able to replace it by a precise formula, just as the description "rate-of-change of $\phi(x)$ with x" yields

(i) $$\phi'(x) = \lim_{h \to 0} \{\phi(x + h) - \phi(x)\}/h.$$

In fact, the formula does not merely replace the description, but makes it precise. If, for instance, we doubt whether $\phi'(1)$ exists, we can replace x by 1 in (i) and investigate the existence of the limit; whereas we cannot examine the "rate-of-change of $\phi(1)$ with 1."

For functions of two variables, two formulas are in common use:

(ii) $$f_x(x, y) = \lim_{h \to 0} \{f(x + h, y) - f(x, y)\}/h$$

and

(iii) $$f_x(a, b) = \lim_{h \to 0} \{f(a + h, b) - f(a, b)\}/h$$

with corresponding formulas for f_y.

Neither is satisfactory. Let us take (ii) first, and ask for what values of x and y it holds. Given any particular f, we can take particular values of x and y, say $x = 2$ and $y = 3$ (or $x = 4$ and $y = 0$, etc.) and investigate the limit. If it exists, what exactly have we defined? Putting $x = 2$ and $y = 3$ in the expression $f_x(x, y)$ we get $f_2(2, 3)$; therefore we have [from formula (ii)] defined $f_2(2, 3)$, $f_4(4, 0)$, etc. But this is not normal usage: most textbooks would say that we have defined $f_x(2, 3)$, $f_x(4, 0)$ etc., and thus these books use the two occurrences of the same symbol x in $f_x(x, y)$ in two quite different ways. This usage is bad in principle, and also leads to practical difficulties. Let, for instance, f be defined by

(iv) $$f(x, y) = x \cdot \sin y \quad \text{for every } x \text{ and } y.$$

This would give

$$f_x(x, y) = \sin y \quad \text{for every } x \text{ and } y,$$

from which

(v) $$f_x(1, 0) = 0.$$

Now, defining f by (iv) is equivalent to defining f by

$$f(w, x) = w \cdot \sin x \quad \text{for every } w \text{ and } x.$$

This would give

$$f_x(w, x) = w \cdot \cos x,$$

from which

$$f_x(1, 0) = 1,$$

contradicting (v).

Definition (iii) leads to similar trouble. Taking f as in (iv), and putting $a = r$ and $b = \theta$ in (iii), we get

$$f_x(r, \theta) = \lim_{h \to 0} \{(r + h) \cdot \sin \theta - r \cdot \sin \theta\}/h = \sin \theta.$$

Common usage, however, would be to write

$$f_r(r, \theta) = \sin \theta$$

because $f(r, \theta)$ is $r \cdot \sin \theta$.

The trouble clearly lies in the use of the subscript, which is not a variable (nor a constant) but a marker to show which of the two arguments of f takes the increment in the expression whose limit we require. A simple and clear notation, already used by Landau, is to use 1 and 2 for subscripts. Thus

$$f_1(a, b) = \lim_{h \to 0} \{f(a + h, b) - f(a, b)\}/h,$$

and

$$f_2(a, b) = \lim_{h \to 0} \{f(a, b + h) - f(a, b)\}/h.$$

Then with the particular f defined in (iv) we have unambiguously

$$f_1(x, y) = \sin y \qquad \text{for every } x \text{ and } y,$$

and

$$f_2(x, y) = x \cdot \cos y \quad \text{for every } x \text{ and } y.$$

Logicians would *expect* (iii) to lead to trouble, because it is incorrect in form: the left-hand side involves x whereas the right-hand side does not.

In practice the invalid notation makes the subject not impossible but merely obscure. The reasons are that many problems involve the formula $f(x, y)$ without ever involving $f(r, t)$ or $f(x, x)$ or $f(y, x)$; and that if we are told that u is a function of x, y, and z we automatically write $u = \phi(x, y, z)$ with arguments in alphabetical order.

With these conventions we can go a long way before trouble obtrudes (further in physics than in geometry, where symmetry might bring $f(x, y)$ and $f(y, x)$ into the same problem); there is then all the more to be put right when it eventually does so.

A clear understanding of the difference between a function and a dependent variable is also necessary for a clear understanding of partial differentiation. If we define f and ϕ by

(vi) $$f(x) = 2x + 3 \quad \text{for every } x$$

and

$$\phi(x) \ = \ \int_{t=0}^{x} (1 + t^2)^{-1} \cdot dt \quad \text{for every } x,$$

then f and ϕ are functions. Indeed, ϕ is the function arctan:

$$\phi(x) = \arctan x.$$

Notice that f is just a "function"; it is not a "function of x," because the formula

$$f(k) = 2k + 3 \quad \text{for every } k$$

is equivalent to (vi). The x and k are merely aids in phrasing the definition: f does not depend on either. The same applies to ϕ; indeed, no-one would call arctan a function of x. Of course, $f(x)$, $\phi(x)$, and arctan x are functions of x; but the distinction in words is subtle, whereas the distinction in concepts is important. We therefore prefer to say not "function of x" but "variable dependent on x": arctan x is variable (it varies when x varies) and it depends on x. Precisely, it is *the value at x* of the function arctan.

If now we write $y = f(x)$, then y is a variable dependent on x. The distinction is needed in differentiating. A function is simply differentiated: The derivative of sin is cos, and we could not properly talk of the derivative of sin with respect to x. A dependent variable, however, must be differentiated with respect to something. The derivative of sin x with respect to x is cos x; its derivative with respect to t is $(\cos x) \cdot dx/dt$. In kinematics, dv/ds is different from dv/dt, and the phrase "the derivative of v" is ambiguous.

Having said this, we must admit that the phrase "function of x" is so common and indeed natural that to avoid it completely would be pedantic. It is best regarded as what Bourbaki calls an *abus de langage;* we may use it if we realize that a "function of x" is not a function but a dependent variable.

If y is a function of x, there is (in any one context) only one function which y can be of x. We may be tempted to denote this function also by y, writing

$$y = y(x).$$

This notation, however, not only is a serious bar to the understanding of the concept of function, but also leads to trouble for functions of more than one variable. If, for example, v and w are related ($v = 1 - w$, say) and if $u = v - w$, then we can correctly write $u = \phi(v, w)$ where ϕ is a certain function: in fact, the function defined by

$$\phi(x, y) = x - y.$$

Also,

$$u = \psi(v, w)$$

where

$$\psi(x, y) = 1 - 2y \quad \text{for every } x \text{ and } y.$$

The functions ϕ and ψ are different; the connection between them is only that $\phi(v, w) = \psi(v, w)$ whenever v and w satisfy the relation $v = 1 - w$; and therefore use of formula

$$u = u(v, w)$$

to denote the relation between u, v and w is an ambiguity. If we are clear about the distinction between functions and dependent variables we shall never be tempted to be thus ambiguous, and, indeed, if everyone made this distinction much of the obscurity which many students feel about partial differentiation would be avoided.

Over-emphasis of geometrical intuition is a more subtle cause of difficulty, because it makes the subject easier at first, the disadvantages not showing up until later. The surface $z = \phi(x, y)$ yields a ready visualization of the behaviour of ϕ, but premature use of the geometrical model may persuade the student that it gives the essential meaning of the binary function, rather than just one possible interpretation. In the geometry, x and y are not merely arguments of a function: they are coordinate variables, and as such have properties not shared by all arguments. They have, for instance, a conventional order: To say that the point $(0, 0, 2)$ lies on the surface $z = \phi(x, y)$ is meaningful, and means that $x = 0$, $y = 0$, $z = 2$ satisfies the equation, and not, for instance, that $z = 0$, $x = 0$, $y = 2$ satisfies it. By contrast, to say that $(0, 0, 2)$ satisfies $2p + v = 3m$ is ambiguous. For this reason I have delayed the geometrical part of the subject to a rather later point than might perhaps have been expected.

Part I

Review of Previous Knowledge

1.

We assume a knowledge of derivatives, and that the student can find a formula for $\phi'(x)$, given one for $\phi(x)$, at least when $\phi(x)$ is not too complicated. For example:

$\phi(x)$	$\phi'(x)$
$\sin x$	$\cos x$
x^n	$n \cdot x^{n-1}$
$y \cdot x^2 + z \cdot x$	$2y \cdot x + z$
$\alpha\{\beta(x)\}$	$\alpha'\{\beta(x)\} \cdot \beta'(x)$

and so on. The last entry in the table is, of course, the chain-rule for differ-entiating a function of a function. This rule we shall use a great deal.

We notice that the formula for $\phi(x)$ may contain other Roman letters besides x. These other letters are called *parameters*. Thus in the formulas above, n, y and z are parameters.

However, in the formula $\psi(y) = y \cdot x^2$, x is a parameter. Then $\psi'(y) = x^2$.

2.

Problems. Find a formula for:

$\phi'(z)$ when $\phi(x)$ is $\quad 2c \cdot x^3$

$\psi'(2)$ when $\psi(x)$ is $\quad x$

$\theta'(v)$ when $\theta(u)$ is $\quad u^2 + 2u \cdot v + v^2$

$\theta'(a)$ when $\theta(a)$ is $\quad a^b$

$\theta'(a)$ when $\theta(b)$ is $\quad a^b$

3.

An expression containing several letters can be regarded as the value of any one of several functions. For example:

$$\phi(x) = y \cdot x^2 + z \cdot x$$
$$\rho(y) = y \cdot x^2 + z \cdot x$$
$$\sigma(z) = y \cdot x^2 + z \cdot x$$

Which of these we use depends on the purpose we have in mind. For in-stance, if we are interested in the rate-of-change of the volume of a cone with the radius of the base we should (remembering that the volume of a cone of height h and radius r is $\frac{1}{3}\pi \cdot r^2 \cdot h$) write

$$\alpha(r) = \frac{1}{3}\pi \cdot r^2 \cdot h.$$

Then the rate-of-change, $\alpha'(r)$, is $\frac{2}{3}\pi \cdot r \cdot h$.

But if we are interested in the rate-of-change of volume with height, we would rather write

$$\beta(h) = \frac{1}{3}\pi \cdot r^2 \cdot h,$$

and investigate $\beta'(h)$, which is $\frac{1}{3}\pi \cdot r^2$.

Illustration. The height of a cylinder whose base is of fixed radius, r cm, is increasing at a rate of 2 cm/sec; let us find the rate-of-increase of its volume. First, we notice that if the rate-of-change of h is 2, then the rate-of-change of $\phi(h)$ is $2\phi'(h)$. This is because h depends on t: say, $h = \eta(t)$. Then $\phi(h)$ depends on t: it equals $\phi\{\eta(t)\}$. Its rate-of-change t is, by the chain-rule,

$$\phi'\{\eta(t)\} \cdot \eta'(t) = \phi'(h) \times 2.$$

Let $\phi(h) = \pi \cdot r^2 \cdot h$. This represents the volume. Then

$$\phi'(h) = \pi \cdot r^2,$$

and so the rate-of-change of volume is

$$2\pi \cdot r^2 \text{ cm}^3/\text{sec.}$$

The radius of another cylinder, of fixed height h cm is increasing at a rate of 2 cm/sec. Let $\psi(r) = \pi \cdot r^2 \cdot h$. Then

$$\psi'(r) = 2\pi \cdot r \cdot h,$$

and so the rate-of-change of volume is

$$4\pi \cdot r \cdot h \text{ cm}^3/\text{sec.}$$

4.

Illustrative problem.   A topless box has length x cm and height y cm. Its width is such that its volume is 4 cm³.

(i)   For a given height, find the least external surface area as the length varies.

(ii)   For a given length, find the least external surface area as the height varies.

(iii)   Find the least external surface area as both vary.

A solution.   The width is $4/x \cdot y$ cm and so the external surface area is

$$4/y + 8/x + 2x \cdot y \text{ cm}^2.$$

For (i) we require the least value of this (for a given y) as x varies through positive values, so we let

$$\phi(x) = 4/y + 8/x + 2x \cdot y,$$

and investigate this by the familiar method. Then

$$\phi'(x) = -8/x^2 + 2y,$$

and we find that the least value of ϕ is given by the one and only value of x which makes the derivative zero. This is found to be $x = 2y^{-1/2}$, and the least value of ϕ is

$$4/y + 8y^{1/2}.$$

This answers (i). For (ii) we investigate ψ where

$$\psi(y) = 4/y + 8/x + 2x \cdot y$$

and we find that

$$\psi'(y) = -4/y^2 + 2x,$$

and that the one and only value of y which makes $\psi'(y)$ zero does in fact give a minimum of ψ. The least value of $\psi(y)$ is

$$4\sqrt{2}\, x^{1/2} + 8/x.$$

We can answer (iii) by finding *either* the least value of $4/y + 8y^{1/2}$ as y varies, *or* the least value of $4\sqrt{2}\,x^{1/2} + 8/x$ as x varies. Let us choose the first of these two ways. The familiar method shows that $4/y + 8y^{1/2}$ is least when $y = 1$; its value is then 12. (When x is such as to give a minimum, $x = 2y^{-1/2}$; and so now $x = 2$. Then the width is 2 cm. Thus the box of minimum area has length 2 cm, width 2 cm, height 1 cm.) If we had chosen the second way we should, of course, have reached the same answer.

5.

Now let us suppose that instead of being asked questions (i), (ii) and (iii) we had been asked only (iii). We could have solved it as before, that is, by finding (in terms of y) the least surface area as x varies, and then finding the least value of *this* as y varies. But we can take a short cut. We used the familiar method; that is, we found the values which made the derivative zero and investigated them. The final result is both a local minimum for x and local minimum for y, and so for the values which we found ($x = 2$ and $y = 1$) both $\phi'(x)$ and $\psi'(y)$ must be zero. (We can check this by evaluating $\phi'(2)$ and $\psi'(1)$ in the formulas above.)

We could therefore have worked as follows:

$\phi'(x) = -8/x^2 + 2y$;   this is zero if and only if $x^2 \cdot y = 4$.

$\psi'(y) = -4/y^2 + 2x$;   this is zero if and only if $x \cdot y^2 = 2$.

Solving these two equations gives $x = 2$, $y = 1$: these are the required values of x and y. Thus for *finding* extrema this method (which amounts to using the two variables "in parallel" instead of "in series") is quicker than the other. We shall see later (in **K5**) that we can develop it to give a test (analogous to the "second-derivative test") for determining what sort of extremum we have found.

6.

Problem. Using both of the above methods, prove that the brick which has the least surface area for a given volume is a cube.

7.

We shall often, especially in chapter **H**, have situations where an equation involving several variables implicitly defines one of them as a function of the others. For example:

$$x + y = 0 \quad \text{defines } y \text{ as } -x,$$

or $\qquad\qquad\qquad p \cdot v = r \cdot t \quad \text{defines } p \text{ as } r \cdot t / v.$

Let us, to begin with, consider just two variables; if $\phi(x, y) = 0$ defines

y as a function of x we say that this function is *implicitly* defined by
the equation. If the result of solving the equation $\phi(x, y) = 0$ for y is
$y = \eta(x)$, we say that this is an *explicit* form of the equation. More often
we say simply that this is a *solution* of the equation, but we must think
carefully just what this means.

Let us consider the situation geometrically. The equation $\phi(x, y) = 0$
is one which a given pair of numbers may or may not satisfy. The set
of all points whose coordinates do satisfy it is the graph of the equation;
and we know that usually such a graph is a curve: If $\phi(x, y)$ is $x^2 + y^2 - 1$,
for instance, the graph is a circle of radius 1 about $(0, 0)$. Now no equation
of the form $y = \eta(x)$ can have this circle as its graph, because the line
$x = 0$ cuts the circle in two points, whereas it cuts the graph of $y = \eta(x)$
in precisely one point: $\{0, \eta(0)\}$. However, we can find a solution which
gives us part of the graph: $y = (1 - x^2)^{1/2}$ is an obvious one; it gives us
the upper half. $y = -(1 - x^2)^{1/2}$ is an equally obvious one. Less obvious
ones include

$$y = \begin{cases} (1 - x^2)^{1/2} & \text{if } 1 \geqslant x \geqslant 0 \\ -(1 - x^2)^{1/2} & \text{if } -1 \leqslant x < 0, \end{cases}$$

and

$$y = (1 - x^2)^{1/2} \qquad \text{if } -\tfrac{1}{10} < x < \tfrac{1}{10}.$$

This last one gives us only a small part of the graph and may seem un-
naturally restricted, but in many problems in the calculus a solution of
this sort is good enough. For example, if we want to find $\eta'(0)$ it is certainly
enough to know $\eta(x)$ whenever

$$-\tfrac{1}{10} < x < \tfrac{1}{10}.$$

Thus we have a "local" solution of our equation: there is a neighborhood
inside which $y = \eta(x)$ if and only if $\phi(x, y) = 0$. The diagram shows
two such neighborhoods (I and II) for
$x^2 + y^2 - 1 = 0$. Neighborhood III,
however, is one in which there is no
solution; this is for the reason we saw
above: in neighborhood III a line parallel to the y-axis can cut the graph in
more than one point.

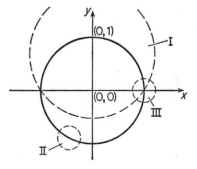

Notice that if (a, b) is a point on the
graph *other than* $(1, 0)$ or $(-1, 0)$, then
there is always a neighborhood of (a, b)
in which there is a solution. We say
then that there is a *local solution* at
(a, b). It is easy to see geometrically whether or not there is a local solution. The characteristic property of the graph of the *explicit* equation
$y = \eta(x)$ is that no vertical line cuts it more than once; and, conversely,

if a curve has this property it is the graph of some explicit equation. Thus if P is a point on the graph of any equation, say $\phi(x, y) = 0$, and if we can find a circle with center P—any circle at all, no matter how small, as long as the radius is not actually zero—such that the part of the given graph inside the circle has the characteristic property, then there is a local solution at P.

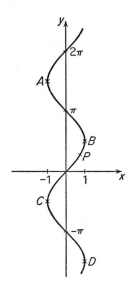

Let us consider similarly some other graphs.

Illustration 1. The graph of $x = \sin y$ is a sine-curve with its axis vertical.

At any point on it other than points like those marked with a cross, there is a local solution for y. If P is any point between B and C, for instance, the solution at P is

$$y = \arcsin x.$$

If Q is any point between A and B, however, the local solution at Q is

$$y = \pi - \arcsin x;$$

and if R is $(\frac{1}{2}, 18\frac{1}{6}\pi)$ the local solution near R is

$$y = 18\pi + \arcsin x.$$

Illustration 2. The graph of $x = y^5 - 10y^2$ is readily drawn. (Most students will find it easiest to draw $y = x^5 - 10x^2$, and then turn the resulting curve on its side.) At any point P on the graph other than O and A (which is actually the point $(-12 \cdot 2^{1/3}, 2^{2/3})$), there will be a local solution, but it cannot be expressed by a formula like the ones we had for the circle and the sine-curve. It is for curves like this that we need an "existence" theorem; that is, a statement that under certain conditions the curve $\phi(x, y) = 0$ does have a local solution at (a, b).

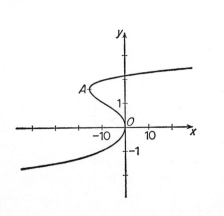

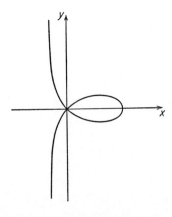

Illustration 3. The graph of

$$2x^3 + 6x \cdot y^2 - 3x^2 + 3y^2 = 0$$

is as in diagram. (The student who is not an adept at curve tracing should just accept this as a fact: we are using the curve only as an illustration.) This shows that the graph of quite a simple equation can cross itself. Naturally, there is no local solution at any point where the curve does so.

Illustration 4. The graph of $|y| = x$ is as in the diagram. (It consists of the parts of the lines $y = x$ and $-y = x$ for which x is non-negative.) Clearly it has no local solution for y at $(0, 0)$.

We have found various types of point where there are no local solutions: points where the tangent is vertical; points where the curve has a sharp corner (and therefore has no tangent); and points where the curve crosses itself (and where, according to the precise definition of tangent which we are using, we might say that the curve has no tangent or that it has several tangents). In any case, if we consider a point P where the curve has a unique non-vertical tangent we avoid these exceptions and in fact it is intuitively clear that there is then a local solution at P. That is, if P is on the curve $\phi(x, y) = 0$, and if the curve has a unique non-vertical tangent at P, then there is a circle about P and a function η such that inside the circle the curves $y = \eta(x)$ and $\phi(x, y) = 0$ are the same.

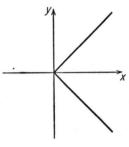

In **D20** we shall find conditions on the function ϕ which ensure that the curve does have a unique non-vertical tangent at (a, b); to do this conveniently we shall need derivatives, though one set of conditions for local solvability not using derivatives will be found in **N2**.

Meanwhile, let us note that although the existence of a unique non-vertical tangent is sufficient to ensure a local solution, it is not necessary.

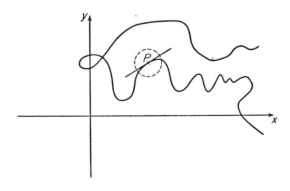

We can have local solutions without. For instance, at $(0, 0)$ the graphs of $y^3 = x$ and $y - |x| = 0$ have, respectively, a vertical tangent and no tangent; nevertheless they have local solutions there, namely $y = x^{1/3}$ and $y = |x|$, respectively.

8.

Questions.

1. Does $\phi(x, y) = 0$ have a local solution for y at (a, b) if $\phi(x, y)$, a and b are, respectively:

$$y^3 - x - 1, 1, 1;$$
$$y^3 - x, 0, 0;$$
$$y^4 - x, 1, 1;$$
$$y^4 - x, 0, 0;$$
$$\tan y - x, 0, 0;$$
$$\tan y - x, 0, \pi;$$
$$\tan y - x, 0, k \cdot \pi, \text{ where } k \text{ is an integer};$$
$$x^4 + y^4 - 1, 0, -1?$$

Give a formula for the solution where possible.

2. Where does $x^2/4 + y^2 = 1$ have a local solution for y?

3. Where does $\tan y - x = 0$ have a local solution for y?

9.

The reader will be familiar with the use of cartesian coordinates in a plane. A similar system can be used in space: the *axes of coordinates* are three mutually perpendicular straight lines intersecting in a point called the *origin*. The coordinates of a point in this system are a trio of numbers; namely, the components in the directions of the axes of the distance of the point from the origin. The axes are (usually) labelled x, y and z, and the coordinates are given in that order.

Thus, if

$$OP = PQ = QS = OT = 1,$$

all angles in the diagram being right-angles, the coordinates of the various points are as follows:

O	$(0, 0, 0,)$
P	$(0, 1, 0,)$
Q	$(1, 1, 0,)$
R	$(1, 0, 0,)$
S	$(1, 1, 1,)$
T	$(0, -1, 0)$

The trio (a, b, c) is said to satisfy the equation $\phi(x, y, z) = 0$ if $\phi(a, b, c)$ does equal zero. The graph of an equation is the set of all points whose coordinates satisfy the equation. Thus P, R, and S are on the graph of

(i) $$x + y - z = 1,$$

but O, Q, and T are not.

The graph of an equation is, in general, a surface, and in particular the graph of a linear equation is a plane. For instance, the graph of (i) is the plane PSR, the graph of $z = 0$ is the plane OPR, the graph of

$$x^2 + y^2 = 1$$

is the cylinder whose axis is the z-axis and whose cross section is a circle of radius 1, and the graph of

$$x^2 + y^2 + z^2 = 1$$

is the sphere with center O of radius 1.

The graph of a set of equations consists of the points whose coordinates satisfy them all; that is, it is the intersection of the graphs of the individual equations. Thus the graph of a pair of equations is, in general, a curve. For instance, the graph of

$$\begin{cases} z = \tfrac{1}{2} \\ x^2 + y^2 + z^2 = 1 \end{cases}$$

is the intersection of the sphere already mentioned by the plane $z = \tfrac{1}{2}$, and so is a circle.

It is usual, when there is no reason not to, to speak of the z-axis as "vertical," and in purely geometrical contexts, where there is no question of the axes being set up in the physical word, "vertical" means simply "parallel to the z-axis," and the "ground-plane" is the plane $z = 0$. In applications, if one of the axes is actually vertical, it is normal to take this axis as the z-axis.

The graph of a binary function, ϕ, is the graph of the equation $z = \phi(x, y)$. This is precisely analogous to the fact that the graph of η in plane cartesian coordinates is the curve $y = \eta(x)$. Moreover, the graph of ϕ has the property that no vertical line can cut it in more than one point. To see this, we reflect that the vertical line through $(a, b, 0)$ does not cut the graph at all if $\phi(a, b)$ is undefined, and cuts it in the one point $\{a, b, \phi(a, b)\}$ if $\phi(a, b)$ is defined.

10.

Other three-dimensional systems are sometimes useful. If in the ground-plane we use polar coordinates r and t instead of cartesian coordinates x

and y (so that $x = r \cdot \cos t$ and $y = r \cdot \sin t$) then the system which uses r, t and z is called a *cylindrical polar* system.

If the coordinates of a point X are the distance, r, of X from O, the t just mentioned, and the angle s between OX and the vertical, then the system which uses r, s and t is called a (spherical) *polar* system.

B

Basic Definitions

1.

Let us recall the problem in **A5**. There are many other problems in which we want to use several variables "in parallel." To do this, it is inconvenient to consider various separate functions, like ϕ and ψ in

$$\phi(x) = 4/y + 8/x + 2x \cdot y = \psi(y).$$

It is better to consider one function like θ in

$$\theta(x, y) = 4/y + 8/x + 2x \cdot y.$$

Such a function as θ is called a *binary* function. Again, instead of the three separate functions in **A3** we could consider ζ where

$$\zeta(x, y, z) = y \cdot x^2 + z \cdot x.$$

Such a function as ζ is *ternary*. In general, if

$$\xi(x_1, x_2, \ldots, x_n)$$

is defined, then ξ is an *n-ary* function. (Other names for *n*-ary functions are "*n*-adic functions," "*n*-place functions," "functions of *n* arguments," "functions of *n* variables.") Thus

$$1\text{-ary} = \text{singulary}$$
$$2\text{-ary} = \text{binary}$$
$$3\text{-ary} = \text{ternary}$$
$$4\text{-ary} = \text{quaternary}$$

and so on. The names are derived from the Latin distributive numerals.

2.

A binary function has two derivatives. If

$$\psi(x, y) = x^2 + 3x + y^2 + 4y$$

then differentiating re x gives $2x + 3$; differentiating re y gives $2y + 4$. We denote the two derivatives by ψ_1 and ψ_2. Thus

$$\psi_1(x, y) = 2x + 3; \qquad \psi_2(x, y) = 2y + 4.$$

Let us recall the definition of derivative of a singulary function:

$$\phi'(x) = \lim_{h \to 0} \{\phi(x + h) - \phi(x)\}/h$$

for every x for which the limit exists. It is obvious what the definitions of the two derivatives of a binary function must be:

$$\psi_1(x, y) = \lim_{h \to 0} \{\psi(x + h, y) - \psi(x, y)\}/h$$

for every (x, y) for which the limit exists;

$$\psi_2(x, y) = \lim_{h \to 0} \{\psi(x, y + h) - \psi(x, y)\}/h$$

for every (x, y) for which the limit exists. Thus ψ_1 and ψ_2 are the derivatives of the "separate" functions which we considered in **A4**. That is, if

$$\theta(x) = \psi(x, b) \quad \text{for each } x$$

then

$$\theta'(a) = \psi_1(a, b);$$

and if

$$\phi(x) = \psi(a, x) \quad \text{for each } x$$

then

$$\phi'(b) = \psi_2(a, b).$$

Similar definitions hold for functions of more variables.

3.

The technique of differentiating *n*-ary functions is the same as for 1-ary functions. Just as

$$\phi(x) = \sin (x + 2) \quad \text{yields} \quad \phi'(x) = \cos (x + 2),$$

so

$$\psi(x, y) = \sin(x + y) \quad \text{yields} \quad \psi_1(x, y) = \cos(x + y).$$

Just as

$$\phi(y) = a \cdot y^2 + b \quad \text{yields} \quad \phi'(y) = 2a \cdot y,$$

so

$$\theta(x, y, z) = x \cdot y^2 + z \quad \text{yields} \quad \theta_2(x, y, z) = 2x \cdot y.$$

And so on.

4.

Problems

(i) $\phi(x, y, z)$ is $x^2 \cdot y + y^2 \cdot z + z^2 \cdot x$. What are

$$\phi_1(3, 1, 2), \quad \phi_3(3, 1, 2), \quad \phi_2(0, 1, 0), \quad \phi_1(0, y, z),$$

$$\phi_2(-x, y, -z), \quad \phi_3(u, v, w), \quad \phi_1(x + y, x - y, 0), \quad \phi_2(y, z, x)?$$

(ii) $\phi(x, y)$ is x^y. What are

$$\phi_1(x, y) \quad \text{and} \quad \phi_2(x, y)?$$

(iii) $\phi(y, x)$ is $x^2 - y^2$. What are

$$\phi_1(y, x), \quad \phi_2(y, x), \quad \phi_1(3, 2), \quad \phi_1(u, v), \quad \phi_1(x, y)?$$

(iv) $\phi(x, y)$ is $x \cdot \exp(\arctan(x^2 - 2y^2)^{1/2})$. What are

$$\phi_1(a, b), \quad \phi_2(2, 1)?$$

(v) $\phi(x, y) = \begin{cases} (x^2 - y^2)^{1/2} & \text{if } x \geqslant y \geqslant 0; \\ 0 & \text{otherwise.} \end{cases}$

What are

$$\phi_1(4, 3), \quad \phi_1(3, 4), \quad \phi_2(1, 1)?$$

5.

If θ is a binary function with derivatives θ_1 and θ_2, then these two derivatives are themselves binary functions and so in their turn have derivatives. The derivatives of θ_1 are naturally denoted by θ_{11} and θ_{12}, and so on. Thus if

$$\theta(x, y) = x^2 + a \cdot x \cdot y - y^2,$$

then

$$\theta_1(x, y) = 2x + a \cdot y;$$

whence $\theta_{11}(x, y) = 2$ and $\theta_{12}(x, y) = a$; and

$$\theta_2(x, y) = a \cdot x - 2y;$$

whence

$$\theta_{21}(x, y) = a \quad \text{and} \quad \theta_{22}(x, y) = -2.$$

6.

Problems

(i) What are θ_{11}, θ_{12}, θ_{21}, and θ_{22} if

$$\theta(x, y) = \cos x \cdot \sin y?$$

(ii) What is $\theta_{13}(u, v, w)$ if

$$\theta(x, y, z) = x^3 \cdot y^2 \cdot z?$$

(iii) Prove that if $\theta(x, y)$ is a cubic in x and y, then

$$\theta_{12}(x, y) = \theta_{21}(x, y)$$

for every x and y.

(iv) What is $\theta_{121}(x, y)$ if

$$\theta(x, y) = y \cdot \cos x?$$

7.

From the answers to **6** it appears as though usually $\theta_{12} = \theta_{21}$. Later (in **M17**) we shall prove that this is in fact a general rule. To be precise, if θ_{12} is continuous at (a, b) and if $\theta_2(x, y)$ exists for every (x, y) near enough to (a, b), then

$$\theta_{21}(a, b) = \theta_{12}(a, b).$$

C

Integration

1.

After differentiation we naturally think of integration. Just as differentiation of a n-ary function is essentially the same as that of a singulary function as long as we treat the arguments one at a time, so integration of n-ary functions involves nothing essentially new. Just as

$$\int_{x=1}^{3} 2x \cdot dx = \left[x^2 \right]_{x=1}^{3} = 8,$$

so

$$\int_{x=1}^{3} y \cdot x \cdot dx = \left[\tfrac{1}{2} y \cdot x^2 \right]_{x=1}^{3} = 4y.$$

Similarly,

$$\int_{y=1}^{3} y \cdot x \cdot dy = \left[\tfrac{1}{2} y^2 \cdot x \right]_{y=1}^{3} = 4x.$$

23

For a precise definition of

$$\int_{x=a}^{b} \theta(x,\, y) \cdot dx,$$

we define, for each y, a function $\xi^{(y)}$ by

$$\xi^{(y)}(x) = \theta(x,\, y) \quad \text{for each } x.$$

Then the integral above is defined to be

$$\int_{x=a}^{b} \xi^{(y)}(x) \cdot dx,$$

which is itself defined in the theory of singulary functions.

Notice that a definite integral re one argument of a function of several arguments is a function of all these arguments *except* the one first mentioned. It is also, of course, a function of whatever arguments the limits of integration may be functions of. For example,

$$\int_{v=0}^{1} \phi(u,\, v,\, w) \cdot dv \quad \text{is a function of } u \text{ and } w,$$

$$\int_{q=a}^{b} \phi(p,\, q) \cdot dq \quad \text{is a function of } a,\, b, \text{ and } p.$$

This means that we may have repeated integrals: For example,

$$\int_{y=0}^{1} \left(\int_{x=0}^{1} 4x \cdot y \cdot dx \right) \cdot dy, \quad \text{which equals} \quad \int_{y=0}^{1} 2y \cdot dy,$$

which equals 1.

Here we have been using the pure functional notation: nothing in our formulas is a function of x unless it is so written. Some writers like to abbreviate by putting, say, $y = \phi(x)$; here y is a variable dependent on x. With this notation we must be careful, for then

$$\int_{x=1}^{3} y \cdot x \cdot dx \quad \text{denotes} \quad \int_{x=1}^{3} \phi(x) \cdot x \cdot dx,$$

and this will not normally be equal to

$$\left[\tfrac{1}{2}\phi(x) \cdot x^2 \right]_{x=1}^{3}.$$

2.

We have considered integrals re the separate arguments. Integrals involving all the arguments together are known as multiple integrals, and it turns out that for most practical purposes they can be reduced to repeated integrals. The technique of this reduction forms a separate subject and is outside the scope of this book; and the evaluation of the repeated integrals requires only the technique used for singulary functions.

3.

Problems. Evaluate

(i) $\int_{x=0}^{1} (x^2 - y^2) \cdot dx$

(ii) $\int_{y=0}^{1} (x^2 - y^2) \cdot dy$

(iii) $\int_{z=0}^{1} (x^2 - y^2) \cdot dz$

(iv) $\int_{y=x}^{2x} (x^2 - y^2) \cdot dy$

(v) $\int_{y=0}^{1} \left(\int_{x=0}^{1} (x^2 - y^2) \cdot dx \right) \cdot dy$

(vi) $\int_{x=0}^{1} \left(\int_{y=0}^{1} (x^2 - y^2) \cdot dy \right) \cdot dx$

(vii) $\int_{x=0}^{1} \left(\int_{y=x}^{2x} (x^2 - y^2) \cdot dy \right) \cdot dx$

(viii) $\int_{x=1}^{2} \phi_1(x, y) \cdot dx$

Find $\psi'(y)$ if $\psi(y)$ is:

(ix) $\int_{x=1}^{2} \cos (x + y) \cdot dx$

(x) $\int_{x=y}^{2y} \cos (x + y) \cdot dx$

(xi) $\int_{x=1}^{2} \phi_1(x, y) \cdot dx$

(xii) $\int_{x=y}^{2y} \phi_1(x, y) \cdot dx$

(xiii) $\int_{x=\alpha(y)}^{\beta(y)} \cos (x + y) \cdot dx$

(xiv) $\int_{x=\alpha(y)}^{\beta(y)} \phi_1(x, y) \cdot dx$

(xv) $\int_{x=\alpha(y)}^{\beta(y)} \theta(x + y) \cdot dx.$

It may be assumed that ϕ and θ are continuous, differentiable, etc.: that is, that they are sufficiently well-behaved for all the integrals involved to exist.

D

The Chain-rule

1.

Let us suppose that we can find the derivative of $\theta(x, y)$ re x. How shall we differentiate, say,

$$\theta(2x^2 - x \cdot y, x \cdot y + x \cdot z) \quad \text{re} \quad x,$$

or, in general,

$$\theta\{\alpha(x), \beta(x)\} \quad \text{re} \quad x?$$

Let us start with a simple case: where x comes into only one of the arguments of θ. For example, let us differentiate

$$\theta\{\alpha(x), y\} \quad \text{re} \quad x.$$

We can reduce this to the familiar singulary function quite easily: For any given y, $\theta(z, y)$ is a function of z, which we may denote by $\phi(z)$. Then

(i) $$\phi'(z) = \theta_1(z, y) \quad \text{for every} \quad z,$$

and $\theta\{\alpha(x), y\}$, the expression which we want to differentiate, is $\phi\{\alpha(x)\}$. This is a (singulary) function of a (singulary) function; and we can differentiate it by the chain-rule. Its derivative re x is

$$\phi'\{\alpha(x)\} \cdot \alpha'(x).$$

By (i), this equals

$$\theta_1\{\alpha(x), y\} \cdot \alpha'(x),$$

which is the required derivative.

Similarly, the derivative of

$$\theta\{x, \beta(y)\} \quad \text{re} \quad y$$

is

$$\theta_2\{x, \beta(y)\} \cdot \beta'(y);$$

the derivative of $\theta\{\phi(x, y), z\}$ re x is

$$\theta_1\{\phi(x, y), z\} \cdot \phi_1(x, y);$$

and so on.

2.

Problems

(i) Differentiate

$$\theta(\sin x, \cos y) \quad \text{and} \quad \theta(\sin y, \cos x) \quad \text{re} \quad x.$$

(ii) $\lambda(x, y)$ is $\log_{x+1} y$ for every positive x and y. Find formulas for the derivatives of λ. Differentiate

$$\lambda(\sin x, \cos y) \quad \text{and} \quad \lambda(\sin y, \cos x) \quad \text{re} \quad x.$$

(iii) Find formulas for the derivatives of

$$\phi[\alpha\{y, \beta(x, y), y\}, \gamma(y, y), \delta\{y, \beta(z, y), y\}]$$

re x and re z.

(iv) $\mu(x, y) = (x^2 + y^2)^{1/2}$. Differentiate

$$\mu(2x + y, 2y - x) \quad \text{re} \quad x.$$

Prove that the derivative re x of $\mu\{\alpha(x), \beta(x)\}$ is

$$\alpha'(x) \cdot \mu_1\{\alpha(x), \beta(x)\} + \beta'(x) \cdot \mu_2\{\alpha(x), \beta(x)\}.$$

3.

The formula in 2(iv) is true in general. A little thought will show that it is to be expected. If x changes and b remains fixed, the rate-of-change of $\mu\{\alpha(x), b\}$ will be

$$\alpha'(x) \cdot \mu_1\{\alpha(x), b\}$$

by the chain-rule. However, if a is fixed and x changes, the rate-of-change of $\mu\{a, \beta(x)\}$ will be

$$\beta'(x) \cdot \mu_2\{a, \beta(x)\},$$

again by the chain-rule.

Hence, if the symbols u and v stand for functions of x:

> if u varies at rate u_x and v is fixed, then
>
> $\qquad \mu(u, v)$ varies at rate $u_x \cdot \mu_1(u, v)$;
>
> if u is fixed, and v varies at rate v_x, then
>
> $\qquad \mu(u, v)$ varies at rate $v_x \cdot \mu_2(u, v)$.

What if u and v both vary? We might well expect $\mu(u, v)$ to vary at the sum of these two rates. Now, if u is $\alpha(x)$, then u_x is $\alpha'(x)$; and if v is $\beta(x)$ then v_x is $\beta'(x)$. Then the rate of change of $\mu\{\alpha(x), \beta(x)\}$ is

$$\alpha'(x) \cdot \mu_1\{\alpha(x), \beta(x)\} + \beta'(x) \cdot \mu_2\{\alpha(x), \beta(x)\}.$$

This is in fact true, and later (in **M15**) we shall prove it. For the moment we shall just state it formally:

THEOREM. If ϕ_1 and ϕ_2 are continuous and if α and β are differentiable, then the derivative re x of

$$\phi\{\alpha(x), \beta(x)\}$$

is

$$\alpha'(x) \cdot \phi_1\{\alpha(x), \beta(x)\} + \beta'(x) \cdot \phi_2\{\alpha(x), \beta(x)\}.$$

This is the chain-rule for functions of two functions.

Throughout this chapter we shall assume, except where the contrary is implied, that the functions considered are well enough behaved for the chain-rule to hold.

4.

Similar results will be true for ternary functions: the derivative re x of

$$\theta\{\alpha(x), \beta(x), \gamma(x)\}$$

is

$$\alpha'(x) \cdot \theta_1\{\alpha(x), \beta(x), \gamma(x)\} + \beta'(x) \cdot \theta_2\{\alpha(x), \beta(x), \gamma(x)\}$$
$$+ \gamma'(x) \cdot \theta_3\{\alpha(x), \beta(x), \gamma(x)\}.$$

5.

The chain-rule is very important. Almost all the theory and practice of the differentiation of n-ary functions depends on it. We can shorten it by using $u, v \ldots$ as abbreviations for $\alpha(x), \beta(x) \ldots$, and u_x for $\alpha'(x)$, etc., as we did in our preliminary discussion above, and h for $\phi(u, v)$.

If we also use h_u as an abbreviation for $\phi_1(u, v)$, etc., the formula becomes

$$h_x = h_u \cdot u_x + h_v \cdot v_x.$$

The corresponding formula for a ternary function is

$$h_x = h_u \cdot u_x + h_v \cdot v_x + h_w \cdot w_x,$$

and so on.

A similar notation can be used for higher derivatives: h_{uu} will denote $\phi_{11}(u, v)$, h_{uv} will denote $\phi_{12}(u, v)$, and so on.

Note. This notation, though convenient, can be ambiguous, unless we are conscious throughout our working that each letter like u denotes a *dependent variable.* If in doubt we can use the fuller notation. Later we shall have occasion to emphasize the distinction between the dependent-variable notation and the fuller, functional notation.

6.

Problems

(i) Find a formula for ϕ' in terms of α_1 and α_2 if

$$\phi(x) = \alpha(x^2, 1/x),$$
$$\phi(x) = \alpha(\sin x, e^x),$$
$$\phi(x) = \alpha(-x, x).$$

(ii) Find formulas for ψ_1 and ψ_2 if $\psi(x, y) = \log_y x$. Hence, find a formula for ϕ' if

$$\phi(x) = \log_{x^2} \sin x.$$

(iii) Prove that the derivative re x of

$$\int_{t=x}^{a} \alpha(t) \cdot dt \quad \text{is} \quad -\alpha(x).$$

Find ψ_1 and ψ_2 in terms of α if

$$\psi(u, v) = \int_{t=u}^{v} \alpha(t) \cdot dt.$$

Find ϕ' in terms of α if

$$\phi(x) = \int_{t=x^2}^{x^3} \alpha(t) \cdot dt.$$

(iv) Find a formula for ϕ' if

$$\phi(x) = \gamma(\cos x, \sin x, x).$$

(v) Calculate $\phi'(0)$ if ϕ is as in (iv), and

$$\gamma_1(1, 0, 0) = 1, \quad \gamma_2(1, 0, 0) = \gamma_3(1, 0, 0) = 0.$$

(**vi**) The volume of a solid of a certain type is $\alpha(x, y, z)$ cm^3 if x cm is its height, y cm its width and z cm its length. It is known that

$$\alpha_1(x, y, z) = y \cdot z/6, \quad \alpha_2(x, y, z) = z \cdot x/6, \quad \text{and}$$
$$\alpha_3(x, y, z) = x \cdot y/6.$$

At a certain instant the length and width of the body are 10 cm and are increasing at 2 cm/sec, and its height is 10 cm and decreasing at 1 cm/sec. What is then the rate-of-change of volume?

7.

Now let us see how we can use the chain-rule.

(i) As a short cut in differentiation. For instance, to differentiate

$$x^2 + x^2 \cdot y^2 + y^2$$

re t if

$$x = r^2 + t^2 \quad \text{and} \quad y = r^2 - t^2.$$

The direct way would be to substitute for x and y, which gives a rather long expression in r and t; and then to differentiate this. The expression we get is

$$(r^2 + t^2)^2 + (r^2 + t^2)^2 \cdot (r^2 - t^2)^2 + (r^2 - t^2)^2$$

and its derivative, after simplification, comes out to be

$$8t^3 \cdot (1 - r^4 + t^4).$$

The short cut is to denote

$$x^2 + x^2 \cdot y^2 + y^2 \quad \text{by} \quad \phi(x, y).$$

Its derivative re t is

$$x_t \cdot \phi_1(x, y) + y_t \cdot \phi_2(x, y), \quad \text{by the chain-rule}$$
$$= 2t \cdot (2x + 2x \cdot y^2) + (-2t) \cdot (2x^2 \cdot y + 2y)$$
$$= 4t \cdot (x - y) \cdot (1 - x \cdot y) = 8t^3 \cdot (1 - r^4 + t^4).$$

(ii) When we are given the rates of change of the dependent variables and want the rate-of-change of the expression as a whole. For example, the height of a cylinder increases at a rate of 0.1 cm/sec, and the radius decreases at a rate of 0.2 cm/sec. What is the rate-of-change of the volume at an instant when the height is 1 cm and the radius is 1 cm? Let the volume be $\phi(r, h)$ cm^3 when the radius is r cm and the height h cm. Then

$$\phi(r, h) = \pi \cdot r^2 \cdot h,$$

and so

$$\phi_1(r, h) = 2\pi \cdot r \cdot h \quad \text{and} \quad \phi_2(r, h) = \pi \cdot r^2.$$

If t denotes time, $r_t = 0.1$ and $h_t = 0.2$. The rate-of-change of $\phi(r, h)$ is

$$r_t \cdot \phi_1(r, h) + h_t \cdot \phi_2(r, h)$$
$$= \pi \cdot r \cdot (2h \cdot r_t + r \cdot h_t)$$
$$= \pi \cdot r \cdot (2h - 2r)/10 = \pi \cdot r \cdot (h - r)/5.$$

Thus at the given instant the rate-of-change of volume is zero.

8.

Problems

   (i) $x = r + t^2$, $y = r - t^2$. Differentiate

$$x^2 + y^2 \quad \text{re} \quad t.$$

   (ii) The radius of a cylinder at time t sec is $t^2 - \frac{1}{2}t + \frac{1}{4}$ cm; its height at that time is $t^2 + \frac{1}{2}t + \frac{1}{72}$ cm. Find the rate-of-change of its volume when $t = 2$.

   (iii) The height of a cone is increasing at a rate a cm/sec, and the radius of the base at a rate b cm/sec. At an instant when the height is h cm and the radius of the base r cm, what is the rate-of-change of the volume?

   (iv) In (iii), $a = 1$, $b = -1$. Find the proportions of the cone when the rate-of-change of the volume is zero; and show that at this instant the volume is at a (local) maximum. That is, show that just before that instant it was increasing, and that just afterwards it will be decreasing.

   (v) The rates of increase of three concurrent edges of a closed rectangular box at time t secs are

$$(\log_e t + t) \text{ cm/sec}, \quad (e^t - t) \text{ cm/sec}, \quad \text{and } (3 + \tfrac{1}{2}t^2) \text{ cm/sec}.$$

When $t = 1$ the sides are all 4 cm long. Find the rates-of-change of the volume and of the surface-area at that instant.

   (vi) The charge in the battery of a car when it has travelled x km in t hours after installation is $72 - x^{3/2} + \frac{1}{2}t$ units. Ten hours after its battery was installed a certain car is going at 25 km/hr, and has covered 225 km since the installation. What is the rate-of-charge of the battery at that instant?

   (vii) A quantity of gas obeys the following law: when its pressure is p dynes/cm^2 and its temperature is $t°$K, then its volume is

$$14t/p \text{ cm}^3.$$

It is in a container which is being heated steadily at a rate of 4°K per second. At the instant when the temperature is 294°K the pressure is 1 dyne/cm^2 and is decreasing at a rate of $\frac{1}{10}$ dyne/cm^2/sec. What is the rate-of-change of volume at that instant?

   (viii) The electric potential at a distance x cm from a charge of c units is c/x units. An instrument for measuring potential moves at a constant speed of one revolution per minute round a circle of radius 100 cm. At the point C, halfway between the center O of the circle and the circumference is a charge. No other charges are near enough to affect the instrument. When the instrument is at a point P, for which the angle COP is a right angle, the charge is 5 units and is increasing at a rate of 1 unit per second. What is the rate-of-change of the reading of the instrument at that instant?

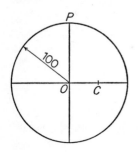

9.

We remarked in **5** that the dependent-variable notation can be ambiguous. Problem 8(vi) gives an example of this. Let us suppose, in general, that $\phi(x, t)$ units is the charge when a car of a certain type has gone x km in t hours after the installation of its battery. If the distance gone by a particular car of this type in t hours is $\xi(t)$ km., then the number of units of charge in its battery at time t is $\phi\{\xi(t), t\}$, whose derivative re t is

(i) $\phi_1\{\xi(t), t\} \cdot \xi'(t) + \phi_2\{\xi(t), t\}.$

On the other hand, the derivative of $\phi(r, t)\, re\, t$ is $\phi_2(r, t)$: that is,

(ii) $\phi_2\{\xi(t), t\}.$

Each of these is, in a sense, a rate-of-change of u with t, if we let u denote the charge; but they cannot *both* be denoted by u_t. We must find another symbol (for example u_t^*) for one of them.

In an applied problem such as this one we bear in mind the meaning of the derivatives. Formula (i) denotes the actual rate-of-charge for a car whose equation of motion is $x = \xi(t)$; (ii) denotes the rate-of-charge for a car standing still.

In *pure* mathematics it is still possible to give a meaning to the derivatives. If

$$u = \phi(x, t) \quad \text{where} \quad x = \xi(t),$$

then (ii) denotes the rate-of-change of u with t due directly to t changing without allowing for the consequent change in x; whereas (i) denotes the rate-of-change of u with t due both directly to t changing and also indirectly through the consequent change in x. Formula (i) is called the *total* derivative, (ii) the *partial* derivative.

$\phi_2(x, t)$ is sometimes called "the rate-of-change of $\phi(x, t)$ with t when x is held constant." This is a trifle misleading, because this derivative is a useful one even in problems where x is *not* constant—the problem under discussion, for instance. "The rate-of-change with t which $\phi(x, t)$ would have if x were constant" is rather better.

In fact, the situation can be treated quite formally. If x depends on t, say $x = \xi(t)$, then $\phi(x, t)$ is equal to $\phi\{\xi(t), t\}$, and so will have a derivative re t. This derivative will, of course, depend on the function ξ; and it is reasonable to describe it as "the derivative of $\phi(x, t)$ re t under the condition $x = \xi(t)$."

This requires only elementary concepts: the only derivative mentioned so far is of a *singulary* function. One possible condition is that x may be constant. It follows, directly from the definition of derivative, that the derivative under this condition is simply $\phi_2(x, t)$, the partial derivative of $\phi(x, t)$ re t.

This situation is fairly common, and a notation has been devised to deal with it. If u is a function of $t, x, y, \ldots$ where $x, y, \ldots$ are themselves functions of t, then the partial derivative of u re t is denoted by $(\partial/\partial t)u$ (or $\partial u/\partial t$) and the total derivative by $(d/dt)u$.

Notice, however, that although the two expressions seem to imply that two *different* operations ($\partial/\partial t$ and d/dt) are applied to the *same* quantity u, in fact the *same* operation (differentiation re t) is applied to two different functions of t [in our problem, to $\phi\{\xi(t), t\}$ and to $\phi(r, t)$].

Another device is, when differentiating re one argument, to use the others as suffixes. For example, if $u = \phi(x, y, z, \ldots, w)$ then

$$\phi_1(x, y, z, \ldots, w)$$

is denoted by $(\partial u/\partial x)_{y, z, \ldots, w}$. Thus instead of $\partial u/\partial t$ for (ii) we find $(\partial u/\partial t)_x$.

Even this notation, although it is already becoming clumsy, can be ambiguous. Let us suppose, for instance, that p, v and t are related (for example, they might represent the pressure, volume and temperature of a given specimen of gas, and the relation might be the gas-law). If $p = \alpha(v, t)$, say, then $\alpha_1(v, t)$ would be denoted by $(\partial p/\partial v)_t$.

Now let us suppose that there is another relation between them (for example, if the gas were kept in a cylinder in such a way that the volume is proportional to pressure and to temperature, we should have $v = k \cdot p \cdot t$ for some k), and that this second relation on its own yields $p = \beta(v, t)$, then $(\partial p/\partial v)_t$ also denotes $\beta_1(v, t)$. This is *not* the same thing as it denoted before.

We do not recommend the use of suffixes as described here unless their meaning is very clearly stated in the context in which they are to be used.

10.

There are one or two other disadvantages of the dependent-variable notation. For instance, if u denotes $\phi(x, y)$ and u_x denotes $\phi_1(x, y)$, we might ask what $\phi_1(0, 2)$ would be in the dependent-variable notation. The usual answer is $(u_x)_{x=0,y=2}$, which is clumsy, or $u_x(0, 2)$, using u_x as though it were a symbol denoting a function, which it is not.

Again, we might ask what $\phi_1(y, x)$ would be in the dependent-variable notation. $(u_x)_{x=y,y=x}$ is not very appealing; $u_x(y, x)$ is, besides being an abuse of the functional notation, hopelessly ambiguous. A safe solution is to define a new variable, v say, to be $\phi(y, x)$, and then $\phi_1(y, x)$ would be naturally denoted by v_y. But this notation fails to show the close connection between u and v.

Thus for problems involving $\phi_1(0, 2)$, etc., or involving both $\phi(x, y)$ and $\phi(y, x)$, the dependent-variable notation is not logically suitable.

The notations u_x and $\partial u/\partial x$ are logically equivalent; although u_x is neater, $\partial u/\partial x$ has the advantage of being immediately recognizable as a derivative. Thus in contexts, such as textbooks of thermodynamics, where derivatives occur occasionally, $\partial u/\partial x$ is the commoner; but in the present book, where letters are used as suffixes only for the present purpose, we shall use u_x.

Let us emphasize, though, that the dependent-variable notation is used only as a convenient abbreviation. In all cases of doubt it should be translated (mentally or literally) into the other.

11.

If ϕ is binary and

(i)
$$\begin{cases} x = \xi(u, v) \\ y = \eta(u, v), \end{cases}$$

we can express $\phi(x, y)$ as a function of u and v. For instance, if

$$\begin{cases} x = u + v \\ y = u - v, \end{cases}$$

then $x^2 + y$ becomes, in terms of u and v,

$$(u + v)^2 + u - v.$$

In general, $\phi(x, y)$ becomes

$$\phi\{\xi(u, v), \eta(u, v)\}.$$

If, then, we define ψ by

$$\psi(u, v) = \phi\{\xi(u, v), \eta(u, v)\},$$

we can regard ψ as a transformation of ϕ under the change-of-variable (i). We can find the derivatives of the new function ψ in terms of those of the old function ϕ:

(ii)
$$\begin{cases} \psi_1(u, v) = \xi_1(u, v) \cdot \phi_1\{\xi(u, v), \eta(u, v)\} \\ \qquad\qquad\qquad + \eta_1(u, v) \cdot \phi_2\{\xi(u, v), \eta(u, v)\}. \\ \psi_2(u, v) = \xi_2(u, v) \cdot \phi_1\{\xi(u, v), \eta(u, v)\} \\ \qquad\qquad\qquad + \eta_2(u, v) \cdot \phi_2\{\xi(u, v), \eta(u, v)\}. \end{cases}$$

This can be written more shortly
$$\psi_1(u, v) = \xi_1(u, v) \cdot \phi_1(x, y) + \eta_1(u, v) \cdot \phi_2(x, y)$$
etc., *provided* that we bear in mind the connection between x, y, u, and v.

12.

If we use the dependent-variable notation and put
$$h = \psi(u, v) = \phi(x, y)$$
then
$$h_x \quad \text{will denote} \quad \phi_1(x, y),$$
$$h_u \quad \text{will denote} \quad \psi_1(u, v),$$
$$x_u \quad \text{will denote} \quad \xi_1(u, v),$$
and so on. Then 11(ii) becomes

(i)
$$\begin{cases} h_u = h_x \cdot x_u + h_y \cdot y_u \\ h_v = h_x \cdot x_v + h_y \cdot y_v. \end{cases}$$

Formulas 11(ii) and 12(i) are like the chain-rule formulas of 4 and 6. There we were really studying a change of variable. Here we are studying a change of a pair of variables.

It is clear what we should have if our functions were ternary. If h depends on x, y and z; and if each of x, y, and z depends on u, v, and w; and if the relevant derivatives exist and are continuous; then
$$h_u = h_x \cdot x_u + h_y \cdot y_u + h_z \cdot z_u$$
and so on.

13.

Illustrative problem. If h depends on x, y, and z and obeys the law

(i)
$$x \cdot h_x + y \cdot h_y + z \cdot h_z = 0,$$

and if x, y, and z are related to three new variables u, v, and w by the laws
$$u = x + y + z$$
$$v = x - y + z$$
$$w = x + y - z,$$
then what is the equation in u, v, and w corresponding to (i)?

A solution:

$$u_x = 1, \qquad u_y = 1, \qquad u_z = 1$$
$$v_x = 1, \qquad v_y = -1, \qquad v_z = 1$$
$$w_x = 1, \qquad w_y = 1, \qquad w_z = -1.$$
$$h_x = h_u \cdot u_x + h_v \cdot v_x + h_w \cdot w_x = h_u + h_v + h_w.$$

Similarly, $$h_y = h_u - h_v + h_w$$

and $$h_z = h_u + h_v - h_w.$$

Therefore the given equation becomes

$$(x + y + z) \cdot h_u + (x - y + z) \cdot h_v + (x + y - z) \cdot h_w = 0.$$

That is,

$$u \cdot h_u + v \cdot h_v + w \cdot h_w = 0.$$

14.

Problems

(i) Variables x, y, z and r, s, t are connected by the equations

$$x = r \cdot \sin s \cdot \cos t, \quad y = r \cdot \cos s \cdot \cos t, \quad z = r \cdot \sin t.$$

What does $x^2 + y^2 + z^2$ become when put in terms of r, s, and t? Find a formula for each of the three derivatives of ϕ if

$$\phi(x, y, z) = x^2 + y^2 + z^2,$$

and for each of the three derivatives of ψ if

$$\psi(r, s, t) = \phi(x, y, z);$$

and verify that they satisfy the equation which we found in **11**.

(ii) A function ϕ satisfies the equation

$$\phi_1(x, y) + \phi_2(x, y) = 0.$$

The change of variables $x = r \cdot \cos t, y = r \cdot \sin t$ transforms ϕ into ψ. What is the corresponding equation satisfied by ψ?

(iii) Using the dependent-variable notation, find formulas for

$$r_x, r_y, t_x, t_y, x_r, x_t, y_r, \quad \text{and} \quad y_t$$

if

$$x = r \cdot \cos t, \qquad y = r \cdot \sin t.$$

(iv) Variables x, y, z and r, s, t are connected as in question (i). Using the dependent-variable notation, find formulas for r_x, r_y, r_z, t_x, etc., and x_r, x_s, etc.

(v) Find u_x, x_u, etc., when $u + v = x$ and $v = x \cdot y$.

(vi) Find u_x, x_u, etc., when $u + v + w = x$, $u + v = x \cdot y$, and $u = x \cdot y \cdot z$.

(vii) Prove that if h is the value at (x, y) of a reasonably well-behaved binary function, and if x and y are related to u and v as in question (v), then

$$h_u = h_x - h_y \cdot y/x, \quad \text{provided} \quad x \neq 0.$$

Find a similar formula for h_u, using the relations of question (vi) instead of (v).

15.

Let us consider in more detail the process of changing a pair of variables, which we touched on in **11**.

In general, we might have,

(i) $$x = \xi(u, v) \quad \text{and} \quad y = \eta(u, v).$$

We can find the derivatives of x and y re u and v by differentiating (i). Let us ask, however, how we could find the derivatives of u and v re x and y. One way might be to solve (i) for u and v and then differentiate; but solving equations is not always practicable. It would not be practicable, for instance, if (i) were

$$x = u^3 + u \cdot v + v^3 \quad \text{and} \quad y = u^5 - u \cdot v + v^5.$$

The following method is not only more practicable but usually shorter. We suppose that (i) has a (local) solution

(ii) $$u = \alpha(x, y) \quad \text{and} \quad v = \beta(x, y).$$

Then it is α_1, α_2, β_1, and β_2 that we need. Let us find α_1 as an example: the others are found similarly. Because (ii) is a solution of (i) then

$$u = \alpha\{\xi(u, v), \eta(u, v)\}$$

for every u and v in some region. Therefore, by the chain-rule,

(iii) $$\alpha_1\{\xi(u, v), \eta(u, v)\} \cdot \xi_1(u, v) + \alpha_2\{\xi(u, v), \eta(u, v)\} \cdot \eta_1(u, v) = 1$$

and

(iv) $$\alpha_1\{\xi(u, v), \eta(u, v)\} \cdot \xi_2(u, v) + \alpha_2\{\xi(u, v), \eta(u, v)\} \cdot \eta_2(u, v) = 0.$$

Eliminating α_2, we obtain

(v) $$\eta_2(u, v) = \alpha_1\{\xi(u, v), \eta(u, v)\} \cdot \{\xi_1(u, v) \cdot \eta_2(u, v) - \xi_2(u, v) \cdot \eta_1(u, v)\}.$$

Therefore

(vi) $$\alpha_1(x, y) = \eta_2(u, v) / \{\xi_1(u, v) \cdot \eta_2(u, v) - \xi_2(u, v) \cdot \eta_1(u, v)\},$$

provided that (ii) holds and the denominator is not zero.

Let us, for the sake of completeness, investigate what happens when the denominator *is* zero. Then, by (v),

$$\eta_2(u, v) = 0, \quad \text{and so} \quad \xi_2(u, v) \cdot \eta_1(u, v) = 0.$$

We can now show that $\xi_2(u, v) = 0$, because if not then $\eta_1(u, v) = 0$ and, by (iv) $\alpha_1(x, y) = 0$, which is incompatible with (iii).

Now (iv) becomes a truism, and (iii) alone is not enough to determine $\alpha_1(x, y)$ [unless $\eta_1(u, v)$ happens also to be zero]. We might, in this case, be able to find $\alpha_1(x, y)$ by some other method, but the trouble may be that equations (i) are not solvable and so α and β do not exist. We shall consider this situation carefully in **N8**.

All this can be done more concisely in the dependent-variable notation.

16.

Sometimes we can have quite a complicated set of connections between variables or, equivalently, quite complicated composite functions. For example, given ternary α and β and binary γ we may want to consider a (binary) function ϕ defined by

$$\phi(x, y) = \alpha[x, \beta\{x, \gamma(x, y), y\}, \gamma(x, y)].$$

We can differentiate ϕ by applying the chain-rule several times. First, let us define ψ by

(i) $$\psi(x, y) = \beta\{x, \gamma(x, y), y\}.$$

Then we have

$$\phi(x, y) = \alpha[x, \psi(x, y), \gamma(x, y)],$$

and so the chain-rule gives simply

(ii)
$$\phi_1(x, y) = \alpha_1[x, \psi(x, y), \gamma(x, y)] + \alpha_2[x, \psi(x, y), \gamma(x, y)] \cdot \psi_1(x, y)$$
$$+ \alpha_3[x, \psi(x, y), \gamma(x, y)] \cdot \gamma_1(x, y)$$
and
$$\phi_2(x, y) = \alpha_2[x, \psi(x, y), \gamma(x, y)] \cdot \psi_2(x, y)$$
$$+ \alpha_3[x, \psi(x, y), \gamma(x, y)] \cdot \gamma_2(x, y).$$

It remains now only to find ψ_1 and ψ_2, which of course we do from (i):

(iii)
$$\psi_1(x, y) = \beta_1\{x, \gamma(x, y), y\} + \beta_2\{x, \gamma(x, y), y\} \cdot \gamma_1(x, y)$$
and
$$\psi_2(x, y) = \beta_2\{x, \gamma(x, y), y\} \cdot \gamma_2(x, y) + \beta_3\{x, \gamma(x, y), y\}.$$

Substituting in (ii) from (iii) gives ϕ_1 and ϕ_2 in terms of the given functions and their derivatives. After a little practice the intermediate step (i) will become unnecessary.

17.

Let us repeat the previous example using the dependent-variable notation.

Put $u = \gamma(x, y)$. Let u_x be $\gamma_1(x, y)$ and u_y be $\gamma_2(x, y)$.

Put $v = \beta(x, u, y)$. Let v_x be $\beta_1(x, u, y)$, v_u be $\beta_2(x, u, y)$, and v_y be $\beta_3(x, u, y)$.

Put $w = \alpha(x, v, u)$. Let w_x be $\alpha_1(x, v, u)$, w_v be $\alpha_2(x, v, u)$ and w_u be $\alpha_3(x, v, u)$.

Then w is our $\phi(x, y)$.

Notice how we have defined w_x, etc. In particular, although

$$v = \beta\{x, \gamma(x, y), y\} = \psi(x, y), \text{ say,}$$

v_x is not $\psi_1(x, y)$. Indeed, let us denote $\psi_1(x, y)$ by v_x^*, and $\psi_2(x, y)$ by v_y^*.

These definitions of w_x, etc., are by no means unnecessary; if we defined u, v, and w only and left the reader to deduce w_x, u_y, etc., from the context, our notation would be ambiguous. He would not know whether v_x meant what we have actually defined it to be, or what we have actually called v_x^*.

Now $\phi(x, y) = w$, where w is a function of x, v, and u. Thus

$$\phi_1(x, y) = w_x + w_v \cdot v_x^* + w_u \cdot u_x,$$

and

$$\phi_2(x, y) = w_v \cdot v_y^* + w_u \cdot u_y.$$

Again, v is a function of x, u, and y. Therefore

$$v_x^* = v_x + v_u \cdot u_x,$$

and

$$v_y^* = v_u \cdot u_y + v_y.$$

Thus

(i) $$\phi_1(x, y) = w_x + w_v \cdot v_x + w_v \cdot v_u \cdot u_x + w_u \cdot u_x,$$

and

(ii) $$\phi_2(x, y) = w_v \cdot v_u \cdot u_y + w_v \cdot v_y + w_u \cdot u_y.$$

Anyone who cannot see why

$$\phi_1(x, y) = w_x + w_v \cdot v_x^* + w_u \cdot u_x$$

is correct, rather than, say,

$$\phi_1(x, y) = w_x + w_v \cdot v_x + w_u \cdot u_x$$

should use the other notation. But this one is more compact and convenient.

18.

We can draw a diagram showing how each variable depends on the others. For example, in Diagram 9, the equation $u = \gamma(x, y)$ corresponds to the two full lines, $v = \beta(x, u, y)$ to the three dotted lines; and $w = \alpha(x, v, u)$ to the remaining three lines. We label the paths as in the diagram. Each term of the required x-derivative corresponds to a path from w to x. For example, the direct path gives w_x. The path via v and u gives $w_v \cdot v_u \cdot u_x$. And so on.

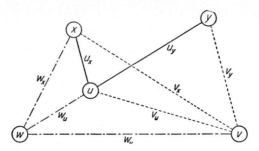

The use of such diagrams often gives a quick and convenient means of writing down the appropriate formula.

19.

Problems

  (i) What are $\phi_1(x, y)$ and $\phi_2(x, y)$ if

$$\phi(x, y) = \alpha\{\beta(x, y), \gamma(x)\}?$$

  (ii) If $w = \phi(x, y) = \alpha(u, v)$, where $u = \beta(x, y)$ and $v = \gamma(x)$; and if $w_x = \phi_1(x, y)$, etc., find w_x and w_y in terms of w_u, w_v, u_x, u_y and v_y.

  (iii) What are $\phi_1(x, y, z)$, $\phi_2(x, y, z)$ and $\phi_3(x, y, z)$ if

$$\phi(x, y, z) = \alpha\{x, \beta(x, y), \gamma(x, z)\}?$$

  (iv) If $w = \phi(x, y, z) = \alpha(x, u, v)$, where $u = \beta(x, y)$ and $v = \gamma(x, z)$; and w_x^* is $\phi_1(x, y, z)$, etc., and w_x is $\alpha_1(x, u, v)$, etc., find w_x^*, w_y^* and w_z^* in terms of w_x, w_u, w_v, u_x, u_v, v_x and v_z.

  (v) Variables x, y, z, u are connected by the relations

$$\left\{ \begin{array}{l} u = \alpha(x, y, z) \\ x = \beta(u, y, z) \end{array} \right.$$

which are sufficient to determine each of u and x as a function of y and z:

$$\left\{ \begin{array}{l} x = \xi(y, z) \\ u = \eta(y, z). \end{array} \right.$$

We denote $\alpha_1(x, y, z)$ by u_x, etc.; we denote $\xi_1(y, z)$ by x_y^*, etc. Find u_y^*, u_z^*, x_y^*, and x_z^* in terms of u_x, x_u, u_y, x_y, u_z and x_z. Hence, find u_y^*, etc., when α and β are given by:

$$\left\{ \begin{array}{l} \alpha(r, s, t) = r \cdot e^s + t \\ \beta(r, s, t) = -e^{r+t} \end{array} \right\} \quad \text{for every } r, s \text{ and } t.$$

(**vi**) Variables x, y, z, u, v, w are connected by the relations

$$\begin{cases} u = \alpha(x, y, z) \\ x = \beta(u, y, z) \\ v = \gamma(x, u) \\ w = \delta(x, y, z, u, v). \end{cases}$$

We denote $\alpha_1(x, y, z)$ by u_x, etc. If we denote

$$\delta[x, y, z, \alpha(x, y, z), \gamma\{x, \alpha(x, y, z)\}]$$

by $\phi(x, y, z)$ then, of course,

$$w = \phi(x, y, z).$$

We denote $\phi_2(x, y, z)$ by w_y^*. We also denote

$$\delta[\beta(u, y, z), y, z, u, \gamma\{\beta(u, y, z), u\}]$$

by $\psi(u, y, z)$; and $\psi_2(u, y, z)$ by $w_y^\dagger$. Find w_y^* and $w_y^\dagger$ in terms of w_x, w_v, u_x, etc.

20.

Let us suppose that x and y are related by the equation

$$x^5 + x^2 \cdot y^3 + y^5 = 1.$$

If this defines y as a differentiable function of x, we can find the derivative by differentiating both sides of the equation, getting

$$5x^4 + 2x \cdot y^3 + 3x^2 \cdot y^2 \cdot y_x + 5y^4 \cdot y_x = 0;$$

whence

$$y_x = -(5x^4 + 2x \cdot y^3)/(3x^2 \cdot y^2 + 5y^4),$$

provided that the denominator is not zero.

This presents an easy way of finding a formula for y_x. And, in general, if the equation $\phi(x, y) = 0$ defines y as a differentiable function of x then, by the chain-rule, provided ϕ_1 and ϕ_2 are continuous,

(i) $$\phi_1(x, y) + \phi_2(x, y) \cdot y_x = 0;$$

whence

$$y_x = -\phi_1(x, y)/\phi_2(x, y)$$

if $\phi_2(x, y) \neq 0$.

This is simple enough if y is defined as a function of x, i.e., if $\phi(x, y) = 0$ is solvable for y. Usually it is not, but we saw in **A7** that often it is locally solvable; and, of course, for finding derivatives a local solution is enough.

Let us now look for conditions that our equation should be locally solvable. We saw that the existence of a non-vertical tangent was a sufficient condition; and this is, of course, equivalent to differentiability of η if $y = \eta(x)$ is the local solution.

Now, if ϕ_1 and ϕ_2 are continuous (which will ensure that the graph of $\phi(x, y) = 0$ is a reasonably well-behaved curve) and if $y = \eta(x)$ is a local solution at (a, b) of $\phi(x, y) = 0$, and if η is differentiable at a, then $\eta(a) = b$ and

$$\phi\{x, \eta(x)\} = 0$$

for every x in the neighborhood of a. Then by the chain rule,

$$\phi_1(a, b) + \phi_2(a, b) \cdot \eta'(a) = 0.$$

This is the equation (i) again and it determines $\eta'(a)$; at least it does so unless

$$\phi_1(a, b) = \phi_2(a, b) = 0.$$

Leaving aside this exceptional case for the moment, we see that if there is a non-vertical tangent at (a, b), then $\phi_2(a, b) \neq 0$. The converse is also true, as we shall prove in **N**: if $\phi_2(a, b) \neq 0$, there is a non-vertical tangent.

Similarly, of course, we can show that (still leaving aside the case $\phi_1(a, b) = \phi_2(a, b) = 0$) the condition for a non-horizontal tangent is $\phi_1(a, b) \neq 0$. Hence, we get the following result.

The curve $\phi(x, y) = 0$ has a tangent at (a, b) if $\phi(a, b) = 0$, and ϕ_1 and ϕ_2 are continuous at (a, b), and they are not both zero there. If $\phi_2(a, b)$ is not zero, the equation is locally solvable for y; if $\phi_1(a, b)$ is not zero, it is locally solvable for x.

Illustration. **Let**

$$\phi(x, y) = 2x^3 + 6x \cdot y^2 - 3x^2 + 3y^2 = 0.$$

Then

$$\phi_1(a, b) = 6a^2 + 6b^2 - 6a$$

and

$$\phi_2(a, b) = 12a \cdot b + 6b.$$

If $\phi_2(a, b) = 0$, then $b = 0$ or $a = -\frac{1}{2}$. If $b = 0$ and (a, b) is on the curve then $2a^3 - 3a^2 = 0$, and so $a = 0$ or $\frac{3}{2}$. If $a = -\frac{1}{2}$ then (a, b) cannot be on the curve, for we cannot have

$$-\tfrac{1}{4} - 3b^2 - 3/4 + 3b^2 = 0.$$

Thus there are just two points on the graph where $\phi_2(a, b) = 0$. Evaluating $\phi_1(a, b)$ at these points, we find that it is zero at $(0, 0)$, non-zero at $(\frac{3}{2}, 0)$.

Thus there is a vertical tangent at $(\frac{3}{2}, 0)$, and at every point except these two there is a local solution for y.

If we trace the curve (see **A7**) we see that the curve crosses itself at $(0, 0)$. In fact, it is commonly true that where

$$\phi_1(a, b) = \phi_2(a, b) = 0,$$

the curve will have either a crossing-point or a cusp (that is, a sharp point), these being the most obvious ways whereby a continuous curve fails to have a tangent.

21.

Problems

1. Find the slope of the curve

$$x^3 - x \cdot y + y^3 = 1$$

at the point (1, 1).

2. At what values of a and b satisfying the equation does

$$x^3 + y^3 - 3x \cdot y = 0$$

fail to be solvable locally at (a, b) for y?

3. Find all vertical and horizontal tangents to the curve

$$x^3 + 3x^2 \cdot y + y^3 = 1.$$

4. Does the curve $x^5 + y^5 = 1$ cross itself?

E

Geometrical Interpretation

1.

Let us consider the graph of a binary function ϕ, and let us direct our attention to one point on it. To start with, let us take a particular example: say

$$\phi(x, y) = x + y^2,$$

and the point $(2, 2, 6)$, which will be on the graph because $\phi(2, 2) = 6$. This is point E in diagram (i).

Consider the plane $y = 2$. This will cut the graph in a curve. This curve is called the *section* of the graph by the plane. In fact, the equation of the graph, in xyz-space, is

$$z = x + y^2$$

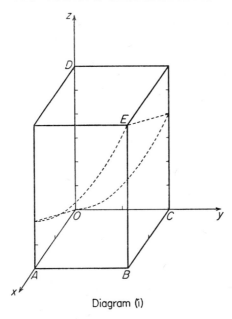

Diagram (i)

and the equations of the curve in which it is cut by the plane $y = 2$ are then

$$\begin{cases} y = 2 \\ z = x + 4 \end{cases} \quad \text{in } xyz\text{-space.}$$

That is, the curve is (obviously) in the plane $y = 2$ and, using the obvious coordinate-system in that plane, its equation is

$$z = x + 4.$$

Diagram (ii) shows the curve in this plane. The slope of the curve at E is the value there of the derivative of $x + 4$ re x, which is 1.

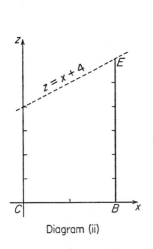

Diagram (ii)

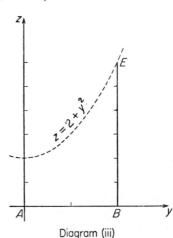

Diagram (iii)

Now consider the plane $x = 2$. The section of the graph of ϕ by this plane will have equations

$$\begin{cases} x = 2 \\ z = 2 + y^2. \end{cases}$$

Diagram (iii) shows this curve in the plane $x = 2$. In this plane, with the obvious coordinate-system, the equation of the curve is

$$z = 2 + y^2.$$

Its slope at E is the value of the derivative of $2 + y^2$ re y when $y = 2$, or 4.

If we consider just how we determined these two slopes, we see that the steps used to obtain the second were as follows: put $x = 2$ in $\phi(x, y)$; differentiate re y; put $y = 2$. Thus the slope is actually $\phi_2(2, 2)$. Similarly, the 1 we obtained earlier was actually $\phi_1(2, 2)$.

2.

The essential point may be clearer in the general case. We start with the graph of ϕ, whose equation will be $z = \phi(x, y)$, and we cut it by the plane $y = b$. The equation in this plane of the curve of section is $z = \phi(x, b)$. Its slope is, in general, $\phi_1(x, b)$, and its slope at E (where $x = a$) is $\phi_1(a, b)$. Similarly, the slope at E of the section of the graph by $x = a$ is $\phi_2(a, b)$.

Thus we have interpreted the derivatives of a binary function as slopes—a pleasing analogy with the interpretation of the derivative of a singulary function as the slope of its graph.

3.

Let us return to the surface $z = x + y^2$ of section 1. It will have a tangent-plane at E. What shall we obtain if we cut this plane by the plane $x = 2$? Clearly, we shall get a line and, indeed, the tangent to the curve in which $x = 2$ cuts the original surface. This tangent we have found: it is the line in $x = 2$ through $(2, 2, 6)$ with slope 4. Similarly, the tangent-plane at E is cut by $y = 2$ in the line through $(2, 2, 6)$ in that plane with slope 1.

Now we can find an equation of the tangent-plane. Because the plane goes through $(2, 2, 6)$ it will have an equation of the form

(i) $$l \cdot (x - 2) + m \cdot (y - 2) + n \cdot (z - 6) = 0,$$

and we have to find $l : m : n$.

This plane cuts $y = 2$ in the line

$$l \cdot (x - 2) + n \cdot (z - 6) = 0.$$

The slope of this line is to be 4; that is, $-l/n = 4$.

The plane cuts $x = 2$ in

$$m \cdot (y - 2) + n \cdot (z - 6) = 0,$$

whose slope is to be 1; that is, $-m/n = 1$. Hence, if $l = -4n$ and $m = -n$, then (i) is an equation of the tangent-plane. Thus the required equation is

$$4(x - 2) + (y - 2) - (z - 6) = 0.$$

That is,

$$4x + y - z = 4.$$

4.

Now let us apply the same method to $z = \phi(x, y)$. It may or may not have a tangent-plane at $(a, b, \phi\{a, b\})$, which fact will not surprise anyone who recalls that the curve $y = \psi(x)$ in two dimensions may or may not have a tangent at $(a, \psi\{a\})$, because ψ may or may not be differentiable at a. If there is a tangent-plane, it will have an equation of the form

$$l \cdot (x - a) + m \cdot (y - b) + n \cdot \{z - \phi(a, b)\} = 0,$$

where the ratios $l:m:n$ are so chosen that the slopes at E of the sections of this plane by $x = a$ and $y = b$, respectively, are $\phi_2(a, b)$ and $\phi_1(a, b)$. Thus

$$-m/n = \phi_2(a, b), \quad \text{and} \quad -l/n = \phi_1(a, b).$$

Then the required equation is

$$(x - a) \cdot \phi_1(a, b) + (y - b) \cdot \phi_2(a, b) = z - \phi(a, b).$$

5.

Problems

(i) Find an equation of the tangent-plane at $(1, 2, -5)$ to the surface

$$z = x^2 + x \cdot y - 2y^2.$$

(ii) Find an equation of the tangent-plane at $(1, 1, 0)$ to the graph of ψ if

$$\psi(x, y) = x^2 - y^2.$$

(iii) Find an equation of the tangent-plane at $(-1, 1, 0)$ to the surface

$$x^2 \cdot y + y^2 \cdot z + z^2 \cdot x = 1.$$

(iv) $\phi_1(x, y)$ and $\phi_2(x, y)$ exist for every x and y. Q is a given point not on the surface $z = \phi(x, y)$. P is a point on the surface for which the distance PQ is stationary. Prove that P is the foot of a normal from Q to the surface.

F

Directional Derivatives

1.

Let us imagine a particle to be moving (in space) over the graph of ϕ, and let us suppose that the x-axis points east. Then if the particle is directly above the point $(a, b, 0)$ and is moving east, its rate-of-climb is $\phi_1(a, b)$ units, because that is the slope of the curve along which it is moving. (By rate-of-climb we mean here rate-of-change of height with horizontal distance gone; not rate-of-change of height with time.) If the particle is moving north, its rate-of-climb, for similar reasons, is $\phi_2(a, b)$ units. If it is moving west or south, its rate-of-climb is $-\phi_1(a, b)$ or $-\phi_2(a, b)$ units, respectively.

Now let us suppose that it is moving in a direction t radians north of east. If it moves a horizontal distance u units, its first two coordinates change from (a, b) to

$$(a + u \cdot \cos t, \, b + u \cdot \sin t),$$

48

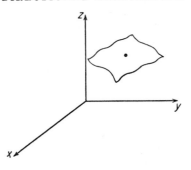

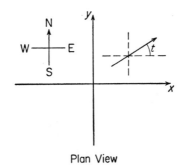

Plan View

and its height from $\phi(a, b)$ to

$$\phi(a + u \cdot \cos t, b + u \cdot \sin t) \quad \text{units.}$$

Let us put

$$\psi(u) = \phi(a + u \cdot \cos t, b + u \cdot \sin t).$$

The initial rate-of-climb is, clearly, $\psi'(0)$ units, and by the chain-rule this is

$$\cos t \cdot \phi_1(a, b) + \sin t \cdot \phi_2(a, b).$$

This expression represents the rate-of-change of ϕ in the given direction. It is usually called the *directional derivative* of ϕ at (a, b) in the given direction. Formally, then, the derivative of ϕ at (a, b) in the direction t is defined to be $\psi'(0)$, where ψ is as above.

Again, let us suppose that a system of coordinates is set up on a hot plate, and the temperature at the point (x, y) is $\theta(x, y)°$C. Then the rate-of-change of temperature with distance in a given direction will be given by the directional derivative of θ in that direction.

2.

Problems

(i) $\alpha(x, y) = x \cdot \cos y + y \cdot \sin x$. Find the following directional derivatives of α: at $(0, 0)$ in the direction corresponding to $t = 1$; at $(1, 1)$ in the direction towards $(0, 0)$; at $(a - b, a + b)$ in the direction of the x-axis (left to right).

(ii) $\beta(x, y) = x^2 + 4x \cdot y + 2y^2$. Find a formula for the directional derivative of β at $(1, 2)$. In what direction is this derivative greatest?

(iii) On a certain mountain range, the height above sea level at a point a km east and b km north of a certain fixed point is

$$1000 + a^2 - 5a \cdot b - b^2 \quad \text{meters.}$$

This holds for every a and b in the region. A skier stands at the point where $a = 4$ and $b = 2$. In what directions may he point his skis if he wants to glide downhill? His companion, wearing no skis, wants to walk horizontally on the mountain-face (that is, along a contour line). In what directions (if any) may he start to move?

(iv) In problem (iii), are there any points where none of the directions are downhill? If so, find them.

(v) A certain mountain range is smooth enough to have a tangent-plane at a certain point. If a mountaineer there were to move northwest, he would find himself climbing up at an angle of 45°, whereas if he were to move northeast, he would be climbing up at an angle of 60°. At what angle would he be climbing if he went south?

3.

In section 1 we had an introduction to functions of position. If the temperature at each point P of a hot-plate is $\theta(P)°$ C, then θ is a function of position. We can, so to speak, turn such functions (in a plane) into binary functions by means of a system of coordinates. For example, we may set up a cartesian system and denote the temperature of the point whose coordinates are (u, v) in this system by $\tau(u, v)$. Then, if P's coordinates are (u, v), $\theta(P) = \tau(u, v)$. If we introduce different systems of coordinates, we get different functions in place of τ.

Illustration. The surface-density $\sigma(P)$ at the point P on a square plate of side 2 cm is, in certain units, numerically equal to the sum of its distances in centimeters from the bottom and right-hand edges:

$$\sigma(P) = p + q \quad \text{if} \quad PM = p \text{ cm} \quad \text{and} \quad QN = q \text{ cm.}$$

[See diagram (i).] If we set up a cartesian system with x-axis AB, y-axis AD, and unit of length 1 cm, and let $\alpha(x, y)$ be the numerical value of the surface-density at (x, y), then

$$\alpha(x, y) = x + y.$$

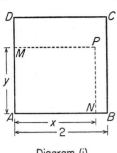

Diagram (i)

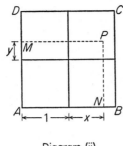

Diagram (ii)

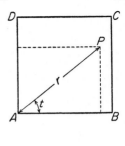

Diagram (iii)

If we set up a cartesian system with origin at the center of the plate, x-axis parallel to AB, and y-axis parallel to AD, and let $\beta(x, y)$ units be the surface-density at the point whose coordinates in *this* system are (x, y), then

$$\beta(x, y) = (x + 1) + (y + 1).$$

If we set up a polar system with pole A and initial line AB and unit of length 1 cm, and let $\gamma(r, t)$ be the numerical value of the surface-density at the point whose coordinates in this system are (r, t), then

$$\gamma(r, t) = r \cdot (\cos t + \sin t).$$

4.

Let us consider another way of specifying a direction. The direction of the arrow in the diagram determines the pair $(\cos p, \cos q)$. These are called the *direction-cosines* of the direction. Because $\cos p = \sin q$, it follows that

$$\cos^2 p + \cos^2 q = 1.$$

Conversely, given any two numbers m and n for which $m^2 + n^2 = 1$, there is one and only one direction which has these for direction-cosines.

There are three reasons why we use the pair $(\cos p, \cos q)$ instead of the single number $\cos p$: (i) to $\cos p = 0$ corresponds not one but two directions; namely $p = \frac{1}{2}\pi$ and $p = \frac{3}{2}\pi$; (ii) direction-cosines generalize easily to three-dimensional space; (iii) direction-cosines are closely related to another useful concept, that of "direction-ratios" which we shall use later (**I9**).

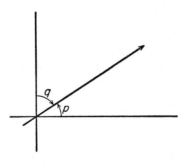

The directional derivative of ϕ at (a, b) in the direction whose cosines are (m, n) is then

(i) $m \cdot \phi_1(a, b) + n \cdot \phi_2(a, b).$

5.

In two dimensions the use of direction-cosines rather than angle p itself is inconvenient, but in three dimensions direction-cosines are very convenient.

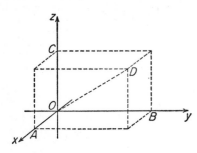

If D is a point in space, let its coordinates in a cartesian system with origin O be (u, v, w). Let A, B and C be the points $(u, 0, 0)$, $(0, v, 0)$, and $(0, 0, w)$ as in the diagram. Then, if p, q, and r are the angles DOA, DOB, and DOC, respectively, they are the direction-angles of OD. They are analogous to the two angles p and q in the two-dimensional case. The direction-cosines are OA/OD, OB/OD, and OC/OD.

It can be proved that if the direction-cosines are l, m, n then

$$l^2 + m^2 + n^2 = 1.$$

Further, the direction (l, m, n) is perpendicular to the direction (l', m', n') if and only if

$$l \cdot l' + m \cdot m' + n \cdot n' = 0.$$

If ϕ is a function of position, we can define a corresponding ternary function τ in the given system of coordinates by

$$\tau(x, y, z) = \phi(P)$$

if P is the point (x, y, z).

We define the directional derivative of τ at (a, b, c) in the direction (l, m, n) to be $\psi'(0)$, where $\psi(u)$ is

$$\tau(a + u \cdot l, b + u \cdot m, c + u \cdot n).$$

By the chain-rule this is equal to

$$l \cdot \tau_1(a, b, c) + m \cdot \tau_2(a, b, c) + n \cdot \tau_3(a, b, c)$$

if τ is well enough behaved. This formula is the analog of 4(i). The analog in spaces of more dimensions is clear.

6.

Illustration. Let us find the directional derivative of ϕ in the direction $(2/\sqrt{6}, 1/\sqrt{6}, -1/\sqrt{6})$ at the point $(2, -1, 2)$ if

$$\phi(x, y, z) = (x + y)^2 + (y + z)^2 + (z + x)^2$$

for every x, y and z.

$$\phi_1(x, y, z) = 2(x + y) + 2(z + x).$$

Therefore $\phi_1(2, -1, 2) = 10$.

$$\phi_2(x, y, z) = 2(x + y) + 2(y + z).$$

Therefore $\phi_2(2, -1, 2) = 4$.

$$\phi_3(x, y, z) = 2(y + z) + 2(z + x).$$

Therefore $\phi_3(2, -1, 2) = 10$.

The derivative in the direction (l, m, n) is

$$(10l + 4m + 10n).$$

The required derivative is

$$(20 + 4 - 10)/\sqrt{6} = 14/\sqrt{6}.$$

Illustrative problem. In what direction should we travel, starting from the point $(2, -1, 2)$, in order to obtain the most rapid rate of increase of $\phi(x, y, z)$, where ϕ is as above?

A solution. The rate of increase in the direction (l, m, n) is

$$10l + 4m + 10n,$$

which is the scalar product of the vectors (l, m, n) and $(10, 4, 10)$. Its value is greatest when these are parallel and in the same direction. That is,

$$l = 10k, \quad m = 4k, \quad n = 10k, \text{ and } k \text{ is positive.}$$

But $l^2 + m^2 + n^2 = 1$; therefore $216k^2 = 1$. And k is positive; therefore $k = 1/\sqrt{216}$. Thus the direction required is

$$(10/6\sqrt{6}, 4/6\sqrt{6}, 10/6\sqrt{6}).$$

7.

If ϕ is a ternary function whose three derivatives are continuous at (x, y, z), its directional derivative there in the direction (l, m, n) will be

$$l \cdot a + m \cdot b + n \cdot c,$$

where a, b, and c are the values at (x, y, z) of the derivatives. If these values are all zero, the directional derivative is zero in all directions. (This occurs at a stationary point.) Otherwise there will be a direction in which it is greatest; and this will be given by

$$l = a/(a^2 + b^2 + c^2)^{1/2}$$
$$m = b/(a^2 + b^2 + c^2)^{1/2}$$
$$n = c/(a^2 + b^2 + c^2)^{1/2}.$$

In the opposite direction it will be least; and in a direction perpendicular to this it will be zero, because the condition that (p, q, r) be perpendicular to (l, m, n) is

$$p \cdot l + q \cdot m + r \cdot n = 0.$$

Now, because $l:m:n = a:b:c$, this is equivalent to

$$p \cdot a + q \cdot b + r \cdot c = 0,$$

and $p \cdot a + q \cdot b + r \cdot c$ is the directional derivative in the direction (p, q, r).

The vector whose direction is that in which the directional derivative at (x, y, z) is greatest, and whose magnitude is that of this greatest directional derivative, is the *gradient* of ϕ at (x, y, z). This vector is

$$(\phi_1\{x, y, z\}, \phi_2\{x, y, z\}, \phi_3\{x, y, z\}).$$

We define a two-dimensional gradient similarly.

The idea of gradient is useful in mathematical physics, especially in the study of electricity and magnetism, and of hydrodynamics.

8.

Problems

(i) Find the gradient of ϕ at $(2, -1)$ if

$$\phi(x, y) = y^2 - 4x.$$

(ii) $\phi_1(a, b)$ and $\phi_2(a, b)$ exist and are not both zero. Prove that the gradient of ϕ at (a, b) is perpendicular to the curve whose equation is $\phi(x, y) = \phi(a, b)$.

(iii) A mountain has the shape of a paraboloid. With suitable axes its equation is

$$z = 300(9x^2 + 16y^2).$$

Find the direction of the line of greatest slope at the point $(4, 3, 12)$ and the angle of slope of that line.

(iv) Find the gradient of ϕ at $(1, 1, 1)$ where

$$\phi(x, y, z) = 2z^3 + (x^2 + y^2) \cdot z.$$

(v) The temperature at the point (x, y, z) is

$$(x + y)^2 + (y + z)^2 + (z + x)^2 \text{ °C}.$$

If a fly is at the point $(2, -1, 2)$, in what direction should it fly in order to achieve the greatest rate of decrease of temperature? If it flies at v cm/sec, and the coordinates are measured in centimeters, what is the greatest initial rate of decrease of temperature which it can achieve?

G

Change of Coordinates

1.

Sometimes we are given a variable in terms of one system of coordinates and are required to express it in terms of another.

Illustrative problem. The value of a certain variable at each point (a, b) in a given cartesian system is $\phi(a, b)$. Another cartesian system has the same origin and its x-axis is the line whose equation in the original system is $y = x \cdot \tan t$. Express the variable as a function of the new coordinates.

A solution. The point whose coordinates in the new system are (u, v) has coordinates

$$(u \cdot \cos t - v \cdot \sin t, \ u \cdot \sin t + v \cdot \cos t)$$

in the old. Therefore, if ψ is the function required,

(i) $\qquad \psi(u, v) = \phi(u \cdot \cos t - v \cdot \sin t, \ u \cdot \sin t + v \cdot \cos t).$

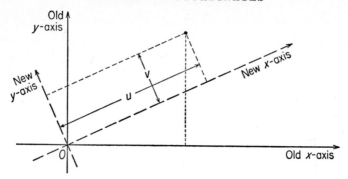

For instance, if

$$\phi(x, y) = x^2 + y^2 + x,$$

then

$$\psi(u, v) = u^2 + v^2 + u \cdot \cos t - v \cdot \sin t.$$

2.

Illustrative problem. The value of a certain variable at each point (a, b) in a given cartesian system is $\alpha(a, b)$. A polar system has its pole at the origin and its initial line along the positive x-axis. Express the variable as a function of the polar coordinates.

A solution. The point whose polar coordinates are (r, t) has cartesian coordinates

$$(r \cdot \cos t, r \cdot \sin t).$$

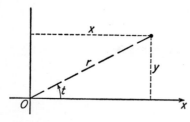

Therefore, if β is the function required,

(i) $\beta(r, t) = \alpha(r \cdot \cos t, r \cdot \sin t).$

For instance, if

$$\alpha(x, y) = x^2 + y^2$$

then

$$\beta(r, t) = r^2.$$

3.

We can go on (in **1**) to find the derivatives of ψ in terms of those of ϕ; and (in **2**) those of β in terms of those of α.

From **1**(i) and the chain-rule,

$$\psi_1(u, v) = \cos t \cdot \phi_1(u \cdot \cos t - v \cdot \sin t, \ u \cdot \sin t + v \cdot \cos t)$$
$$+ \sin t \cdot \phi_2(u \cdot \cos t - v \cdot \sin t, \ u \cdot \sin t + v \cdot \cos t),$$

and

$$\psi_2(u, v) = -\sin t \cdot \phi_1(u \cdot \cos t - v \cdot \sin t, \ u \cdot \sin t + v \cdot \cos t)$$
$$+ \cos t \cdot \phi_2(u \cdot \cos t - v \cdot \sin t, \ u \cdot \sin t + v \cdot \cos t).$$

From 2(i) and the chain-rule,

$$\beta_1(r, t) = \cos t \cdot \alpha_1(r \cdot \cos t, r \cdot \sin t) + \sin t \cdot \alpha_2(r \cdot \cos t, r \cdot \sin t),$$

and

$$\beta_2(r, t) = -r \cdot \sin t \cdot \alpha_1(r \cdot \cos t, r \cdot \sin t) + r \cdot \cos t \cdot \alpha_2(r \cdot \cos t, r \cdot \sin t).$$

4.

More generally, suppose that we have two systems of coordinates, and that, given any point—say the point (u, v) in the first system—we can find its coordinates (x, y) in the second system. This means that we know x and y in terms of u and v. For instance, if the systems are cartesians and polars, as in 2, then

$$x = u \cdot \cos v \quad \text{and} \quad y = u \cdot \sin v.$$

In general,

(i) $$x = \xi(u, v), \qquad y = \eta(u, v).$$

We can find the derivatives of x and y re u and v by differentiating (i); we can find the derivatives of u and v re x and y by the method of **D15**.

5.

Problems

(i) The temperature at the point x km east and y km north of a certain oasis is

$$(x^2 - 2x \cdot y + 3y^2 + 17) \ °C.$$

This holds for each point in the desert. Find a formula for the temperature in terms of a system of polar coordinates, with its pole at the oasis, its initial line running east, and with unit of length 1 km. Find the rate-of-change of temperature (in degrees per kilometer) at the point whose polar coordinates are $(1, \pi/3)$ in a direction directly away from the oasis, and at the point $(2, 2\pi/3)$ towards one's right-hand side when one's back is towards the oasis.

(ii) A variable has the value $x \cdot e_y - x \cdot y$ at the point (x, y) of a cartesian system. At the point (r, t) of a polar system whose pole is at the origin and whose initial line is the x-axis it has the value $\theta(r, t)$. Find a formula for $\theta_1(r, t)$.

(iii) The variable of problem (ii) has the value $\zeta(r, t)$ at the point (r, t)

of a polar system with its pole at $(0, 1)$ and initial line up the y-axis and polar angle measured anti-clockwise. Find a formula for $\zeta_2(r, t)$.

(iv) x, y, z are cartesian coordinates and r, s, t polar coordinates related as in **D14**(i). The humidity at the point whose cartesian coordinates are x, y, z is $\phi(x, y, z)$ units. If

$$\phi_1(1, \sqrt{3}, 2) = 3, \ \phi_2(1, \sqrt{3}, 2) = -2, \text{ and } \phi_3(1, \sqrt{3}, 2) = 1,$$

find the rate-of-change of humidity with distance at the point whose cartesian coordinates are $(1, \sqrt{3}, 2)$: (a) in the direction of increasing r (and constant s and t); (b) in the direction of decreasing t (and constant r and s).

6.

Illustrative problem. What does h_{rt} become when transformed into cartesian coordinates by the transformation

$$x = r \cdot \cos t, \ y = r \cdot \sin t?$$

A solution. $h_r = h_x \cdot x_r + h_y \cdot y_r = h_x \cdot \cos t + h_y \cdot \sin t$. Then

$$h_{rt} = h_{xt} \cdot \cos t - h_x \cdot \sin t + h_{yt} \cdot \sin t + h_y \cdot \cos t$$
$$= (h_{xx} \cdot x_t + h_{xy} \cdot y_t) \cdot \cos t - h_x \cdot \sin t$$
$$+ (h_{yx} \cdot x_t + h_{yy} \cdot y_t) \cdot \sin t + h_y \cdot \cos t$$
$$= \{(h_{yy} - h_{xx}) \cdot \sin t \cdot \cos t + h_{xy} \cdot \cos^2 t - h_{yx} \cdot \sin^2 t\} \cdot r$$
$$- h_x \cdot \sin t + h_y \cdot \cos t.$$

7.

Problems

(i) What does h_{xx} become when transformed into polar coordinates by the transformation in **6**?

(ii) What does the expression $h_{xx} + h_{yy}$ become?

(iii) $\theta(x, y) = \phi(x - y, x + y)$ for every x and y. If

$$\phi_{11}(u, v) - \phi_{22}(u, v) = 0$$

for every u and v, what is the corresponding condition on θ?

(iv) The value of a variable at the point whose cartesian coordinates are x, y, z is

$$x^2 - 2y + y \cdot z.$$

Find a formula for the variable in terms of a spherical polar system, with pole at the origin, initial line along the z-axis, and initial plane $y = 0$. Thus, if r, s, t are the polar coordinates of the point (x, y, z), then

$$x = r \cdot \sin s \cdot \cos t,$$
$$y = r \cdot \sin s \cdot \sin t, \quad \text{and}$$
$$z = r \cdot \cos s.$$

(v) If x, y, z are cartesian coordinates, and if

$$\begin{cases} x = p \cdot \cos t \\ y = p \cdot \sin t, \end{cases}$$

then p, t, z are called *cylindrical* coordinates. Find the cylindrical equation corresponding to the cartesian equation

$$h_{xx} + h_{yy} + h_{zz} = 0.$$

(vi) Find the polar equation corresponding to the cartesian equation

$$h_{xx} + h_{yy} + h_{zz} = 0.$$

[Use the same relations as in problem (iv).]

Note. The results of problems (ii) and (vi) are important and worth remembering.

8.

Let us suppose that we are interested in functions of two coordinate-variables x, y and that

(i) $$u = x + y.$$

Then (x, u) forms a pair of coordinate-variables (probably in a rather unusual system), and any function of (x, y) is also a function of (x, u) and vice versa. For instance,

$$\begin{cases} x^2 + y^2 = x^2 + (u - x)^2, \text{and} \\ u \cdot \cos x = (x + y) \cdot \cos x. \end{cases}$$

In general, given a binary function ϕ,

$$\phi(x, y) = \phi(x, u - x),$$

and we can express $\phi(x, y)$ directly as a function θ of (x, u) by defining θ as follows:

$$\theta(x, u) = \phi(x, u - x).$$

Then $\phi(x, y) = \theta(x, u)$ whenever (i) is satisfied. Thus $\phi_1(x, y)$ and $\theta_1(x, u)$

are, so to speak, derivatives re x of $\phi(x, y)$ and $\theta(x, u)$, respectively. There is no reason, of course, why they should be equal. In fact, if we take $\phi(x, y)$ to be $x^2 + y^2$, then

$$\theta(x, u) = x^2 + (u - x)^2.$$

Hence,

$$\phi_1(x, y) = 2x, \qquad \theta_1(x, u) = 2x - 2(u - x),$$

and these are not the same.

Why trouble to point out the obvious? Because if we use the dependent-variable notation it is not so obvious. For example, if $h = x^2 + y^2$ we deduce $h_x = 2x$. But then also

$$h = x^2 + (u - x)^2$$

which seems to give

$$h_x = 2x - 2(u - x).$$

In this case the notation $(\partial h/\partial x)_y$ and $(\partial h/\partial x)_u$ will distinguish between them (see **D9**), but in more complicated cases even this will not.

The moral is: If we are using the dependent-variable notation for changing from one set of variables to another, we must keep the two sets of variables quite distinct.

9.

Problem. At the point O there is a missile-tracker, which measures the height, h km, and angle of elevation, a radians, of a missile, and records $h \cdot \tan a$ on a dial. Find the rate-of-change of the reading on this dial if the missile is moving with speed v km/sec, (i) directly towards O, (ii) horizontally towards O, (iii) vertically downwards.

Another dial on the tracker records $\sigma(a, b)$, where b km is the horizontal distance of the missile from O and σ is some binary function with continuous derivatives. The rates-of-change of the reading on this dial when the missile is moving with speed v km/sec in directions (i) and (ii) are 3 and -1 units/sec, respectively. Find the rate-of-change when the missile moves with speed w km/sec vertically downwards.

Interdependent Variables

1.

It often happens that the state of some object depends on three variables which are mutually dependent. For example, the properties of a given quantity of gas depend on its temperature, volume, and pressure. But these are not independent: if we fix any two, the third is determined. For example, if the gas is at a controlled temperature in a rigid vessel (so that the volume is controlled) then the pressure will be fixed. If the gas is at a controlled temperature in a cylinder with a given weight on the piston (so that the pressure is controlled), then the volume will adjust itself to the appropriate value. If we want the gas to have a chosen pressure in a chosen vessel, there will be (usually) only one temperature at which this will happen.

The relation between the three variables, pressure, volume, and temperature, is called the "gas law." Various gas laws have been devised, the simplest of which is Boyle's law. This law describes the behavior of a "perfect gas"—a theoretical substance which real gases approximate at low pressures and high temperatures. Boyle's law states that if p denotes pressure, v volume, and t temperature, there is, for a given quantity of a given gas, a number r for which

$$p \cdot v = r \cdot t.$$

Thus, if p and t are chosen, v adjusts itself to the value $r \cdot t/p$.

Another gas law is Van der Waals' law:

$$\left(p + \frac{a}{v^2}\right) \cdot (v - b) = r \cdot t$$

for some constants a and b, depending on the type of gas but not on its pressure, volume, or temperature.

Another example of interdependent variables is provided by direction-cosines. Direction-cosines (l, m, n) are not independent but obey the law

$$l^2 + m^2 + n^2 = 1.$$

Yet another example is provided by a system of coordinates which is occasionally useful, namely the "areal" system. The framework consists of a fixed triangle ABC. The coordinates of a point P in the plane of the triangle are (u, v, w), where u units is the area of the triangle ABP if ABP is clockwise, but is minus this area if ABP is anti-clockwise; v and w are obtained similarly from BCP and CAP. Then u, v, and w are not independent, but add up to the number of units in the area of the triangle ABC. If the units are so chosen

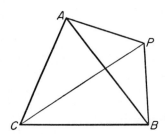

that this triangle has unit area, then

$$u + v + w = 1.$$

For example, the coordinates of C, A, B, and the centroid of ABC are

$$(1, 0, 0), \quad (0, 1, 0), \quad (0, 0, 1) \quad \text{and} \quad (\tfrac{1}{3}, \tfrac{1}{3}, \tfrac{1}{3}),$$

respectively. There are many other examples of interdependent variables.

2.

Let us return to Boyle's law. Each of the three variables is a function of the other two:

(i) $p = r \cdot t/v, \qquad v = r \cdot t/p, \qquad t = p \cdot v/r.$

Thus each may have two derivatives:

$$p_t = r/v, \qquad p_v = -r \cdot t/v^2.$$

In general, if x, y and z are variables so related that

(ii) $\qquad\qquad x = \xi(y, z), \qquad y = \eta(z, x), \qquad z = \zeta(x, y),$

then each may have two derivatives. The derivatives of x are $\xi_1(y, z)$ and $\xi_2(y, z)$, and so on.

We cannot, of course, write down just *any* three equations connecting x, y, and z. For example,

(iii) $\qquad\qquad x = y + z, \qquad y = x^2 + z^2, \qquad z = x - y$

would not do. If the first equation is $x = y + z$, then the next one *must* be $y = x - z$, (or, of course, $y = -z + x$; or something equivalent to these). Given any one, the other two are determined. The test for this is that if we substitute from one into another the result must be a truism.

Consider (i): Substituting $v = r \cdot t/p$ into $p = r \cdot t/v$ we have

$$p = r \cdot t/(r \cdot t/p),$$

which is a truism: that is, it is true for every possible t and p. (Zero is not a possible value of t or p, because a gas cannot have zero temperature or pressure.) If, however, we do the same for (iii), that is, substitute $y = x^2 + z^2$ in $x = y + z$, we obtain

$$x = x^2 + z^2 + z,$$

which is *not* a truism.

Thus, if (ii) really represents a connection between three variables, we must have

$\qquad x = \xi\{\eta(z, x), z\} \quad$ for every possible x and z,

$\qquad x = \xi\{y, \zeta(x, y)\} \quad$ for every possible x and y,

$\qquad y = \eta\{z, \xi(y, z)\} \quad$ for every possible y and z,

and so on.

3.

Problems

(i) From $p \cdot v = 3t$ we deduce

$$p = \pi(v, t), \quad v = \phi(t, p), \quad \text{and} \quad t = \tau(p, v).$$

Evaluate

$$\pi_1(3, 1), \quad \phi_1(1, 1), \quad \tau_1(1, 3), \quad \pi_2(2, 4), \quad \phi_2(4, 6), \quad \tau_2(6, 2).$$

(ii) (a) Wherever $\phi(1, m, n) = 0$, $l = \lambda(m, n)$.

(b) Wherever $l = \lambda(m, n)$, $\phi(l, m, n) = 0$.

(Assume that $\phi(l, m, n)$ and $\lambda(m, n)$ are defined for every l, m, n.) From which (if either) of these statements can we deduce that

$$\phi\{\lambda(m, n), m, n\} = 0 \quad \text{for every } m \text{ and } n?$$

Answer a similar question where $\phi(l, m, n)$ and $\lambda(m, n)$ are defined for every *positive* l, m, and n and are positive, and we want to deduce that

$$\phi\{\lambda(m, n), m, n\} = 0 \quad \text{for every positive } m \text{ and } n.$$

(iii) $l^2 + m^2 + n^2 = 1$. Find the various derivatives of these variables re one another.

(iv) Find the mutual derivatives of the variables in Van der Waals' equation.

(v) $x^3 \cdot y + y^5 \cdot z^3 + z \cdot x = 0$. Find the various derivatives of these variables re one another.

(vi) In (ii), $\phi(1, 1, 1) = 0$, $\phi_1(1, 1, 1) = 7$, $\phi_2(1, 1, 1) = -3$ and $\phi_3(1, 1, 1) = 0$. Find $\lambda(1, 1)$ and $\lambda_1(1, 1)$.

(vii) Equations 2(ii) hold. Prove that

$$\xi_1(y, z) \cdot \eta_2(z, x) = 1,$$

whenever x, y, and z satisfy 2(ii), and that

$$\xi_1(y, z) \cdot \eta_1(z, x) + \xi_2(y, z) = 0,$$

whenever x, y, and z satisfy 2(ii).

(viii) Equations 2(ii) hold. Prove that

$$\zeta_1(y, z) \cdot \eta_1(z, x) \cdot \zeta_1(x, y) = \xi_2(y, z) \cdot \eta_2(z, x) \cdot \zeta_2(x, y) = -1.$$

(ix) $x^3 + x^2 \cdot y + y^5 = 0$ whenever $y = \eta(x)$. Find $\eta'(x)$.

(x) $\phi(x, y) = 0$ whenever $y = \eta(x)$. Find $\eta'(x)$.

4.

If $x = \xi(y, z)$, $y = \eta(z, x)$, and $z = \zeta(x, y)$, then in dependent-variable notation, we should denote $\xi_1(y, z)$ by x_y, and so on. Then the formulas of problems (vii) and (viii) become

$$x_y \cdot y_x = 1, \qquad x_y \cdot y_z + x_z = 0,$$

and

$$x_y \cdot y_z \cdot z_x = x_z \cdot z_y \cdot y_x = -1.$$

Notice that we have proved these only under certain conditions, namely that x, y, and z are related as described in the problems.

Another situation in which $x_y \cdot y_x = 1$, as the reader may recall, is where $x = \alpha(y)$ and $y = \beta(x)$, α and β being mutually inverse differentiable functions. Here it is natural to denote $\alpha'(y)$ by x_y and $\beta'(x)$ by y_x.

However, it is not *universally* true that $x_y \cdot y_x = 1$. For example if

$$x = 2y + v, \qquad u = y - 2v$$

represent a change of variables from (x, u) to (y, v), then $x_y = 2$. Also $5y = u + 2x$, and so $y_x = \frac{2}{5}$.

Also familiar is the situation where x is a function of y and y is a function of z:

$$x = \xi(y), \qquad y = \eta(z).$$

Then x is also a function of z:

$$x = \xi\{\eta(z)\}.$$

By the chain-rule, $x_z = x_y \cdot y_z$ (if the functions in question are differentiable). If $\xi(\eta)$ has an inverse, then $z_x = 1/x_z$ (as above).

Thus, in *this* case, $x_y \cdot y_z \cdot z_x = 1$, *not* -1.

5.

Problems

(i) u, v, w, x, y, z are variables so related that any one is a (differentiable) function of the other five. u_x, etc., have their obvious meanings—for instance, if $u = \phi(v, w, x, y, z)$, then u_x denotes $\phi_3(v, w, x, y, z)$. Prove that:

$u_v \cdot v_u = 1$, and similarly for any pair of the variables;

$u_v \cdot v_w \cdot w_u = -1$, and similarly for any trio of the variables;

$u_v \cdot v_w \cdot w_x \cdot x_u = 1$, and similarly for any quartet of the variables;

$u_v \cdot v_w \cdot w_x \cdot x_y \cdot y_u = -1$, and similarly for any quintet of the variables;

and $u_v \cdot v_w \cdot w_x \cdot x_y \cdot y_z \cdot z_u = 1$.

(ii) Prove that if $x_1, \ldots, x_n$ are related like the six variables in problem (i), and if $1 < r \leqslant n$, then

$$(x_1)_{x_2} \cdot (x_2)_{x_3} \cdot \ldots \cdot (x_r)_{x_1} = (-1)^r.$$

6.

From variables connected by one relation, let us turn to variables connected by more than one relation. The most important situation is where three variables are connected by two relations.

For instance, we might want to consider points on the curve of intersection of the plane

$$x - 2y + 3z = 6,$$

with the surface (actually a cubic cylinder)

$$z = x^3.$$

If the point (u, v, w) lies on these two surfaces, then the variables u, v, w satisfy the two relations

$$u - 2v + 3w = 6, \qquad w = u^3.$$

Then, in general, any one of them can be expressed in terms of any other. In terms of u,

$$v = \tfrac{3}{2}u^3 + \tfrac{1}{2}u - 3, \qquad w = u^3.$$

In terms of w,

$$u = w^{1/3}, \qquad v = \tfrac{1}{2}w^{1/3} + \tfrac{3}{2}w - 3.$$

In terms of v, we have to solve a cubic equation to get explicit formulas for u and w.

Again, let us suppose that we have a gas which obeys the law $p \cdot v = 2t$ (a case of Boyle's law). Let us suppose that the gas is in a container with a certain elasticity and a certain coefficient of expansion, so that when filled with gas at pressure p units and temperature $t\,°$K, its volume is given by

$$v = t^{1/2} \cdot (1 + p)^{-1}.$$

When the gas is in the container, both these relations are satisfied, so again we can find any of the three variables as a function of any other. For example,

$$t = \tfrac{1}{4}p^2 \cdot (1 + p)^{-2} \qquad v = \tfrac{1}{2}p \cdot (1 + p)^{-2}.$$

In general, if three variables satisfy two relations, we can find any one in terms of any other. We shall leave until Part II (Chapter **N**) the question of exactly when this can be done; here we shall investigate only what happens when it can be done; and indeed only when the functions which we get are differentiable.

For instance, if $\alpha(x, y, z) = 0$ and $\beta(x, y, z) = 0$ and if these can be solved in terms of x:

$$y = \eta(x), \qquad z = \zeta(x),$$

we should be able to find the derivatives of η and ζ in terms of those of α and β. And indeed we can, because

$$\alpha\{x, \eta(x), \zeta(x)\} = \beta\{x, \eta(x), \zeta(x)\} = 0$$

for every possible x.

Differentiating re x,

$$\alpha_1\{x, \eta(x), \zeta(x)\} + \alpha_2\{x, \eta(x), \zeta(x)\} \cdot \eta'(x) + \alpha_3\{x, \eta(x)_1 \zeta(x)\} \cdot \zeta'(x) = 0$$

and similarly for β. These two equations can be solved for $\eta'(x)$ and $\zeta'(x)$.

Illustrative problem. Find the rate-of-change of height with abscissa (that is, x-coordinate) for a point moving on the intersection of

$$x - 2y + 3z = 6 \quad \text{and} \quad z = x^3 - y.$$

One method would be to solve for y and z in terms of x and differentiate re x. This would involve solving a cubic in this example and could not be done in most examples. So we suppose that $y = \eta(x)$ and $z = \zeta(x)$ is the solution. Then

$$x - 2\eta(x) + 3\zeta(x) = 6 \quad \text{and} \quad \zeta(x) = x^3 - \eta(x)$$

for every x. Then

$$1 - 2\eta'(x) + 3\zeta'(x) = 0 \quad \text{and} \quad \zeta'(x) = 3x^2 - \eta'(x).$$

Then

$$\zeta'(x) = \tfrac{1}{5}(6x^2 - 1).$$

This is the required rate when the abscissa is x.

7.

Now let us suppose that we have one fundamental relation connecting our three variables, and we want to investigate what happens when various secondary relations hold.

For example, we might have a fixed surface $z = x^3 - y$, and consider the curves of intersection of this with various planes. Or we might have a gas obeying Boyle's law and want to consider its behavior under various conditions—in a certain container, at constant pressure, at constant volume, at constant temperature, etc.

In general, let $\alpha(x, y, z) = 0$ be the fundamental relation. From this, y can theoretically be found as a function ψ of z and x, and the derivative of this function can be found as follows:

$$\alpha\{x, \psi(z, x), z\} = 0$$

for every x, y and z. Then

$$\alpha_1\{x, \psi(z, x), z\} + \alpha_2\{x, \psi(z, x), z\} \cdot \psi_2(z, x) = 0.$$

If y is such that $\alpha(x, y, z) = 0$, then

$$\alpha_1(x, y, z) + \alpha_2(x, y, z) \cdot \psi_2(z, x) = 0.$$

Hence, if $z = c$ and the fundamental relation is obeyed,

(i) $$\alpha_1(x, y, c) + \alpha_2(x, y, c) \cdot \psi_2(c, x) = 0.$$

$\psi_2(z, x)$ is the (partial) derivative of y re x (under the fundamental relation).

Now let us suppose that we have a secondary relation $\beta(x, y, z) = 0$ and that the two between them are equivalent to $y = \eta(x)$ and $z = \zeta(x)$. For different β's we shall, of course, get different η's and ζ's. Two important special cases are where the secondary relation is equivalent to "y is constant" or "z is constant." Let us consider the second of these: $\beta(x, y, z)$ is $z - c$. Then

$$\alpha\{x, \eta(x), \zeta(x)\} = 0 \quad \text{and} \quad \zeta(x) - c = 0$$

for every x, so that

$$\alpha\{x, \eta(x), c\} = 0$$

for every x. Then

$$\alpha_1\{x, \eta(x), c\} + \alpha_2\{x, \eta(x), c\} \cdot \eta'(x) = 0$$

for every x, and so
$$\alpha_1(x, y, c) + \alpha_2(x, y, c) \cdot \eta'(x) = 0$$
whenever the two relations are obeyed.

Comparing with (i), we see that $\eta'(x) = \psi_2(c, x)$. $\eta'(x)$ is the derivative of y re x when z is constant and equal to c (under the fundamental relation).

Hence, if there is one relation between x, y, and z, the partial derivative of y re x is the same as the derivative of y re x when z is constant.

8.

Problems

(i) x, y, z obey the relations $z = x^2 + y^2$ and $x = x^3 + y^3$. Find the derivative of z re x.

(ii) x, y, z obey the relations $z = \alpha(x, y)$, $\beta(x, y) = 0$. Find a formula for the derivative of z re x.

(iii) The point $(1, 2, 3)$ is on both surfaces $z = \phi(x, y)$ and $z = \theta(x, y)$.
$$\theta_1(1, 2) = 1, \quad \theta_2(1, 2) = -1, \quad \phi_1(1, 2) = 2, \quad \phi_2(1, 2) = 3;$$
Find the slope at $(1, 2, 3)$ of the curve of intersection of the surfaces.

(iv) A specimen of gas obeys the law $v = \alpha(t, p)$; a container obeys the law $v = \beta(t, p)$. Solving $\alpha(t, p) = \beta(t, p)$ for p yields $p = \gamma(t)$. The gas is put inside the container. Find the rate-of-change with temperature of the volume of the gas-filled container in terms of t, γ, and the derivatives of α and β.

9.

We now consider the gas laws in some detail. Let us first recall what is meant by *specific heat*. The specific heat of a substance at t °C under given conditions is the number of units of heat required to change the temperature of unit mass of the substance from t °C to $(t + 1)$ °C under those conditions.

This is a fairly common elementary definition. We have defined "specific heat at t °C" instead of just "specific heat," and we have said "change the temperature from t °C to $(t + 1)$ °C," instead of just "raise the temperature by one degree," because specific heat may vary with temperature. It may take more heat to raise the temperature of a piece of iron from 0°C to 1°C than from 10°C to 11°C, for instance.

But the preceding definition does not *really* give the specific heat at t °C. What it gives is the average specific heat between t °C and $(t + 1)$ °C. Let us suppose, for example, that the specific heat was so sensitive to temperature, and that its value was required so accurately, that the amount of heat required for a change from t °C to $(t + \frac{1}{10})$ °C was appreciably different from the amount for a change from $(t + \frac{9}{10})$ °C to $(t + 1)$ °C. Then a better value for the specific heat at t °C would be ten times the former amount. The amount of heat required to bring unit mass of the substance from, say, 0°C to a given temperature under given conditions is a function of that given temperature. Let us call that function ϕ, so that at x °C the unit mass has absorbed $\phi(x)$ units of heat. Then the amount of heat required to change the temperature from t °C to $(t + h)$ °C is

$$\phi(t + h) - \phi(t) \quad \text{units.}$$

Thus our first suggestion for the specific heat gave the value

$$\phi(t + 1) - \phi(t).$$

The second, and better, one gave

$$\{\phi(t + \tfrac{1}{10}) - \phi(t)\}/\tfrac{1}{10}.$$

By the same argument,

$$\{\phi(t + \tfrac{1}{100}) - \phi(t)\}/\tfrac{1}{100}$$

would be better still. Best of all would be

$$\lim_{h \to 0} \{\phi(t + h) - \phi(t)\}/h,$$

which is $\phi'(t)$.

Thus specific heat is the rate-of-change with temperature of the amount of heat absorbed.

10.

Let us suppose that we have equal amounts of the same gas at the same temperature in containers of equal size, the first container being completely rigid, the second being a cylinder closed by a piston exerting constant pressure. If we heat the containers, supplying the same amount of heat to each, the changes in temperature will be appreciably different for the two containers. One way to see this is to imagine that the piston is fixed while the gas is heated. Then the second specimen of gas behaves like the first. Now, without allowing heat to enter or escape, release the piston and let it move until the pressure is down to the original value. Then, as experiment (or the laws of physics) tells us, the temperature will decrease.

Thus, if we measure the specific heat of the gas (a) in a rigid container and (b) in a cylinder with a moving piston, we shall get two different answers. The specific heats measured under conditions (a) and (b) are known as the specific heat at *constant volume* (c_v) and the specific heat at *constant pressure* (c_p): they are the two *principal* specific heats.

Unit mass of a given gas will, when in a certain state, have a certain internal energy. This amount of energy, then, is a function of the pressure, volume, and temperature of the gas. But the gas will obey a gas law (for instance, Boyle's law if it is a "perfect" gas) connecting these three variables. Therefore the internal energy can be expressed as a function of any two of the variables: let us suppose that it is $\kappa(v, t)$. Now, when heat is supplied, some of it may go to increase the internal energy, some of it may go to do work—if the gas expands, it does mechanical work against the external pressure—and some may go to produce electricity, light, sound, etc. (as in a thunderstorm). We shall consider the case where the only work done is the work against pressure, and where no light, sound, etc. are produced. Let the gas law obeyed by unit mass of the gas be $v = \beta(t, p)$. Let the gas be in the state (a, b, c)—that is, let its pressure be a units, its volume b units, and its temperature c units, and let it undergo a change at constant pressure, ending in state (a, v, t). The heat absorbed will be the sum of the change in internal energy and the mechanical work of expansion. If $\phi(t)$ units of heat are required to change the state from (a, b, c) to (a, v, t), then

$$\phi(t) = \kappa(v, t) - \kappa(b, c) + a \cdot (v - b)$$
$$= \kappa\{\beta(t, a), t\} - \kappa(b, c) + a \cdot \{\beta(t, a) - b\}.$$

We saw in section 9 that the specific heat at temperature t degrees was $\phi'(t)$ units. Thus, at temperature t degrees, the specific heat at constant pressure for a units of the gas is

$$\kappa_1\{\beta(t, a), t\} \cdot \beta_1(t, a) + \kappa_2\{\beta(t, a), t\} + a \cdot \beta_1(t, a).$$

Now let us consider a change at constant volume instead of constant pressure. Here no mechanical work is done and so if $\phi(t)$ units of heat are required to change the state to (p, b, t),

$$\phi(t) = \kappa(b, t) - \kappa(b, c).$$

Thus, at temperature t degrees, the specific heat at constant volume for b units of the gas is

$$\kappa_2(b, t).$$

The principal specific heats at state (p, v, t) of the gas are

(i) $\quad \begin{cases} \kappa_1(v, t) \cdot \beta_1(t, p) + \kappa_2(v, t) + p \cdot \beta_1(t, p) \text{ and} \\ \kappa_2(v, t). \end{cases}$

In the dependent-variable notation, if we denote $\kappa(v, t)$ by u, these formulas are generally written as

$$c_p = (\partial u/\partial t)_p + p \cdot (\partial v/\partial t)_p$$

and

$$c_v = (\partial u/\partial t)_v.$$

11.

Problems

(i) An imaginary gas obeying Boyle's law has internal energy $c \cdot p^2 \cdot v^{-1} \cdot t^{1/2}$ units per unit mass when its pressure, volume, and temperature are p, v, and t units, respectively. Find its specific heats at constant pressure and at constant volume.

(ii) The gas in (i) is now enclosed in a spring-loaded vessel which is such that the volume is proportional to the square root of the pressure. Under these conditions, what is the specific heat?

(iii) If $\kappa(v, t)$ units is the internal energy per unit mass of a certain gas which obeys Van der Waals' law, what are the specific heats at constant volume and at constant pressure of the gas?

12.

We may be interested in the behavior of a gas when some external condition is imposed on it. We had an instance in problem 11(ii), the external condition being that $v = k \cdot p^{1/2}$ for some constant k. When this happens, we have two relations between the three variables (because the gas law still holds and so we can, theoretically, express any one of the three in terms of any other). In this particular case

$$p \cdot v = r \cdot t \quad \text{and} \quad v = k \cdot p^{1/2}.$$

Therefore

$$t = \frac{k}{r} \cdot p^{3/2} = \frac{v^3}{r} \cdot k^2, \quad p = \left(\frac{v}{k}\right)^2 = \left(\frac{r}{k} \cdot t\right)^{2/3}, \quad v = k \cdot p^{1/2} = (r \cdot k^2 \cdot t)^{1/3}.$$

An alternative condition which we might have imposed on the gas is that the change should be *adiabatic;* that is, that there should be no loss or gain of *heat* during the change. (There will in general be a change of *temperature.*)

13.

We know, by experiment (or by the kinetic theory) that for many gases the ratio of the principal specific heats is constant (that is, independent of p, v, and t). For gases for which this ratio is constant, we have one extra relation between the variables; and for gases which have this property and obey Boyle's law we are able to find completely the relations between the variables for adiabatic changes. Adiabatic changes are important—for example, in the theory of sound waves and in high-speed flight—so let us proceed.

Boyle's law is $p \cdot v = r \cdot t$, so for a "perfect" gas

$$\beta(t, p) = r \cdot t \cdot p^{-1}, \quad \text{giving} \quad \beta_1(t, p) = r \cdot p^{-1}.$$

Then, by **10**(i),

(i) $$\kappa_1(v, t) \cdot \tau \cdot p^{-1} + \kappa_2(v, t) + r = g \cdot \kappa_2(v, t)$$

for some g.

For adiabatic changes any one of the three variables is a function of any other one. In particular, p is a function of v, say $p = \phi(v)$. Because no heat is absorbed, the sum of the change in u and the work done will be zero. Thus if the state changes from (a, b, c) to (p, v, t), then

$$\kappa\{v, v \cdot \phi(v)/r\} - \kappa(b, c) + \int_{x=b}^{v} \phi(x) \cdot dx = 0.$$

Differentiating re v,

$$\kappa_1\{v, v \cdot \phi(v)/r\} + \kappa_2\{v, v \cdot \phi(v)/r\} \cdot \{\phi(v)/r + v \cdot \phi'(v)/r\} + \phi(v) = 0.$$

That is,

$$\kappa_1(v, t) + \kappa_2(v, t) \cdot \{p/r + v \cdot \phi'(v)/r\} + p = 0.$$

Then, by (i)

$$g \cdot \kappa_2(v, t) + \kappa_2(v, t) \cdot v \cdot \phi'(v)/p = 0,$$

That is,

$$\phi'(v)/\phi(v) + g/v = 0.$$

and so the derivative re v of $\ln \{\phi(v) \cdot v^g\}$ is zero. Thus this logarithm is constant, and so $\phi(v) \cdot v^g$ is constant. Therefore, $p \cdot v^g$ is constant (where g is c_p/c_v).

This equation and $p \cdot v = r \cdot t$ determine completely the adiabatic behavior of the gas. From them we can find any one of the three variables in terms of any other.

14.

Problem. The internal energy $\kappa(v, t)$ of a certain gas is independent of v. The gas obeys Boyle's law. Prove that the difference between its specific heats is constant.

Increments and Differentials

INCREMENTS

1.

We have seen that if the surface $z = \phi(x, y)$ has a tangent-plane at the point $\{a, b, \phi(a, b)\}$, then an equation of this plane is

(i) $\qquad (x - a) \cdot \phi_1(a, b) + (y - b) \cdot \phi_2(a, b) = z - \phi(a, b).$

The height of the plane above $(a + h, b + k, 0)$, that is, the value of z given by (i) when $x = a + h$ and $y = b + k$, is

$$\phi(a, b) + h \cdot \phi_1(a, b) + k \cdot \phi_2(a, b).$$

If we imagine a point to be on the plane and vertically above $(a, b, 0)$ and if that point moves on the plane until it is vertically above $(a + h, b + k, 0)$, then its change in height will be

$$h \cdot \phi_1(a, b) + k \cdot \phi_2(a, b).$$

Let us call this quantity $\Delta^* z$.

If the surface is not too sharply curved, $\Delta^* z$ is a good approximation to the change in height which the point would undergo if it moved not on the tangent-plane but on the surface itself to a position vertically above $(a + h, b + k, 0)$. Let us call *this* change Δz. The smaller h and k, the better the approximation. In fact, for most of the functions which we come across in practice,

(ii) $(\Delta z - \Delta^* z)/(h^2 + k^2)^{1/2} \to 0$ as $(h, k) \to (0, 0)$.

The idea of a *pair* of numbers tending to zero is a new one, and we shall consider it at length in chapter **M**. Meanwhile, it can be thought of graphically as follows:

$$\psi(h, k) \to l \quad \text{as} \quad (h, k) \to (0, 0)$$

means that we can make $\psi(h, k)$ as near to l as we like by taking (h, k) near enough to $(0, 0)$; that is, by making $(h^2 + k^2)^{1/2}$ small enough.

We have interpreted Δz as a change of height on a surface because we were considering the graph of ϕ. But, in general, Δz is simply the change in $\phi(x, y)$ when x changes from a to $a + h$ and y from b to $b + h$. $\Delta^* z$ is a convenient approximation to it, which is not only easy to calculate but is linear in h and k, so that the way in which it varies with h and k is especially simple.

2.

Illustration. If $\phi(x, y) = x^2 + y^2$, then $\Delta^* z = 2a \cdot h + 2b \cdot k$. For this simple function it is easy to calculate Δz: we get

$$2a \cdot h + 2b \cdot k + h^2 + k^2.$$

To verify 1(ii) we merely note that $(h^2 + k^2)^{1/2} \to 0$ as $(h, k) \to (0, 0)$.

3.

Illustrative problem. By approximately how much may an error of 1 per cent in each factor affect a product of two factors?

A solution. Let $\phi(x, y) = x \cdot y$. Let $h = a/100$ (that is, 1 per cent of a), and $k = b/100$. Then

$$\Delta^* z = b \cdot a/100 + a \cdot b/100 = 2a \cdot b/100.$$

The answer is, then, "by 2 per cent."

4.

Formulas similar to those of 1 hold for ternary and higher functions. For example, if ϕ is ternary we may write

$$\Delta z = \phi(a + h, b + k, c + l) - \phi(a, b, c),$$

and
$$\Delta^* z = h \cdot \phi_1(a, b, c) + k \cdot \phi_2(a, b, c) + l \cdot \phi_3(a, b, c).$$
Then, if ϕ is reasonably well-behaved,
$$(\Delta z - \Delta^* z)/(h^2 + k^2 + l^2)^{1/2} \to 0 \quad \text{as} \quad (h, k, l) \to (0, 0, 0).$$

5.

Problems

(i) Find formulas for Δz and for $\Delta^* z$ in terms of h and k if
$$\phi(x, y) = x^2 + x \cdot y - y^2, \quad a = 0, \quad b = 1,$$
and calculate Δz and $\Delta^* z$ if $h = 10^{-3}$ and $k = 10^{-4}$.

(ii) The length, height, and width of a box are measured and found to be 125 cm, 41 cm, and 63 cm, respectively. The possible errors in these measurements are 0.1 cm, 1 cm, and 1 cm, respectively. The length of the diagonal is calculated. What is the approximate percentage possible error in the result due to the inexactness of the measurements?

(iii) Find the approximate percentage change in
$$\frac{u^{1/2}}{(u^2 + v^2)^{1/4}} \cdot (u \cdot \cos a + v \cdot \sin b)$$
caused by simultaneously changing a from $45°$ to $46°$, b from $45°$ to $44\frac{1}{2}°$, u from 20 to 20.08, and v from 15 to 15.06.

DIFFERENTIABILITY

6.

Formula 1(ii) may be written

(i) $\{\phi(a + h, b + k) - \phi(a, b) - h \cdot \phi_1(a, b) - k \cdot \phi_2(a, b)\}/(h^2 + k^2)^{1/2} \to 0$,

as $(h, k) \to (0, 0)$.

There is an interesting uniqueness property here; we cannot have

(ii) $\{\phi(a + h, b + k) - \phi(a, b) - h \cdot u - k \cdot v\}/(h^2 + k^2)^{1/2} \to 0$

as $(h, k) \to (0, 0)$, unless $u = \phi_1(a, b)$ and $v = \phi_2(a, b)$.

To see this, we put $k = 0$; then (i) gives
$$\{\phi(a + h, b) - \phi(a, b) - h \cdot u\}/|h| \to 0 \quad \text{as} \quad h \to 0,$$
and so
$$\{\phi(a + h, b) - \phi(a, b)\}/h \to u \quad \text{as} \quad h \to 0.$$

We see that $\phi_1(a, b)$ exists and equals u. Similarly, $\phi_2(a, b) = v$.

Thus a function which satisfies (ii) for some u and v is 1- and 2-differentiable at (a, b) and satisfies (i). Such a function is said to be *differentiable* at (a, b).

7.

In **6** we defined differentiability for binary functions. The definition for n-ary functions, in general, is obvious. If $n = 1$, ϕ is differentiable at a if, and only if, $\phi'(a)$ exists (and this is why the word "differentiable" was chosen). To see this, we reflect that for singulary ϕ, **6**(i) becomes

$$\{\phi(a + h) - \phi(a) - h \cdot u\}/|h| \to 0 \quad \text{as} \quad h \to 0,$$

which will be true if, and only if,

$$\{\phi(a + h) - \phi(a)\}/h \to u \quad \text{as} \quad h \to 0.$$

Of the various possible generalizations of 1-ary differentiability, the one given here is the most useful. The existence of $\phi_1(a, b)$ and $\phi_2(a, b)$ would also be a generalization of 1-ary differentiability (in fact, a weaker one, because it is implied by ours) but would not be convenient. For instance, existence of $\phi_1(a, b)$ and $\phi_2(a, b)$ does not imply the continuity of ϕ at (a, b), as an example will show, whereas if **6**(i) is true, then clearly

$$\phi(a + h, b + k) - \phi(a, b) \to 0 \quad \text{as} \quad (h, k) \to (0, 0).$$

That is, ϕ is continuous at (a, b)

However, if ϕ_1 or ϕ_2 is *continuous* at (a, b), (and, of course, the other exists there) then ϕ is differentiable there: we prove this in **M18**. This gives us, in practice, the easiest way of testing for differentiability. It soon becomes clear that most of the functions which we come across in practice (functions built up by addition, multiplication, subtraction, division, and the use of trigonometric, exponential, and logarithmic functions) are differentiable everywhere in their domains of definition.

The commonest functions (apart from discontinuous ones) which are not differentiable are those which require two or more formulas to define them. For example, if

$$\phi(x, y) = \begin{cases} \dfrac{x^3 - y^3}{x^2 + y^2} & \text{if} \quad x^2 + y^2 \neq 0 \\ 0 & \text{if} \quad x^2 + y^2 = 0 \end{cases}$$

then ϕ is not differentiable at $(0, 0)$. Notice, however, that $\phi_1(0, 0)$ and $\phi_2(0, 0)$ exist.

Those who like to think or work graphically will find the following fact helpful: ϕ is differentiable at (a, b) if, and only if, the surface whose equation is $z = \phi(x, y)$ has a non-vertical tangent plane at $\{a, b, \phi(a, b)\}$. This is an analog of the familiar fact that a singulary function α is differentiable at a if, and only if, its graph has a non-vertical tangent at $\{a, \alpha(a)\}$. It is, of course, a theorem of analytical geometry, rather than of the calculus; its proof rests on a precise definition of tangent-plane, and it is almost obvious if we take the following definition of tangent-plane.

DEFINITION. A non-vertical plane U through a point P of a surface is a *tangent-plane* to the surface at P (re a given system of coordinates) if the vertical distance from a point Q on the surface to U divided by the horizontal distance from P to Q tends to zero as this horizontal distance tends to zero.

It is not hard to show that if U is a tangent-plane in one system, it is a tangent-plane in any other in which it is not vertical; then we simply call it a tangent-plane at P. It can be shown that the surface cannot have more than one tangent-plane at P, and that our definition is equivalent to the more purely geometrical one obtained by defining U to be a tangent-plane at P if the direction-ratios of the plane PQR tend to those of U as Q and R tend to P on the surface.

It develops that differentiability, though a weaker property than that of having continuous first-order derivatives, is strong enough to ensure that the chain-rule holds. To be precise, we shall eventually (in **M15**) prove the rule in the following form.

Chain-rule. If $\xi(a) = b$ and $\eta(a) = c$, if $\xi'(a)$ and $\eta'(a)$ exist, and if ϕ is differentiable at (b, c), then the familiar formula holds. This is, of course,

$$\psi'(a) = \phi_1(b, c)\cdot\xi'(a) + \phi_2(b, c)\cdot\eta'(a),$$

where $\psi(x)$ denotes $\phi\{\xi(x), \eta(x)\}$.

The conditions for the general theorem (for m n-ary functions) are similar.

Differentiability is also enough for the "$\phi_{12} = \phi_{21}$" theorem: If ϕ_1 and ϕ_2 are differentiable at (a, b) then $\phi_{12}(a, b) = \phi_{21}(a, b)$, as we shall prove in **M17**.

8.

The student who is already familiar with the concept of *differential* for singulary functions may omit sections **8–13**. In these sections we deal with singulary differentials, as a preparation for the binary and eventually the n-ary case.

We start by considering the curve $y = x^{1/3}$. It is simply the curve $y = x^3$ with x and y interchanged: that is, it is a cubic curve turned on its side. It goes through the origin and its tangent there is vertical.

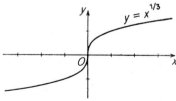

Let us consider the value of the derivative when $x = 0$. By definition, this is

$$\lim_{h \to 0} \{(0 + h)^{1/3} - 0^{1/3}\}/h = \lim_{h \to 0} h^{-2/3}$$

provided that the limit exists. But the limit does not exist, because $h^{-2/3} \to \infty$ as $h \to 0$. Thus our idea that the value of the derivative yields the slope of a graph is true only where the tangent is not vertical.

Although it is perhaps rather exceptional for the graph of a function to have a vertical tangent, more general curves quite commonly do so: for example, the circle $x^2 + y^2 = 1$, has two vertical tangents; $y - x = \sin (y + x)$, an infinite number. Thus it would be convenient to be able to include the vertical case with the others in some way. One way would be to extend our number system to include ∞; and to define $\lim_{h \to 0} h^{-2/3}$ (and other similar expressions) to exist and equal this ∞. This can be done, but needs care.* We shall describe an alternative way.

9.

We are used to representing points in *space* by coordinates (x, y, z). The coordinates of a point are a *trio* of numbers because points in space form a *three*-dimensional system. Similarly, points in a *plane* form a *two*-dimensional system which can be represented by *pairs* of numbers as coordinates. And cartesian coordinates are not the only ones: there are also polar coordinates and other systems.

The idea is not so familiar, but points on a *line* form a *one*-dimensional system, and can be represented by coordinates, each of which is a *single* number. In one-dimensional cartesians (or polars) the number will be the distance from a fixed point on the line, the origin (or pole).

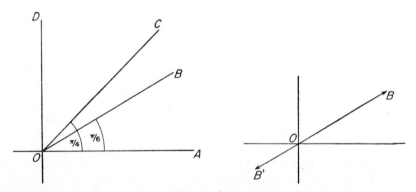

* See H. A. Thurston, *Differentiation and Integration*, chapter V. Blackie, 1961.

Now it is not only systems of *points* which can be represented by coordinates: "Tangential coordinates" or "line-coordinates," for instance, are coordinates of *lines*. Let us consider a one-dimensional system of lines: the set of all lines in a plane through the origin. We could define the slope of each line of the system to be its coordinate. Thus in the diagram the coordinate of OA is 0, of OB is $3^{-1/2}$, and of OC is 1. This system of coordinates has a disadvantage, in that OD has no coordinate. Therefore, instead of using the slope, we use the *direction-ratios*. The direction-ratio of a line is defined to be the ratio of the direction-cosines of either direction on it. A line has, of course, just two directions on it, as shown, for instance, by the two arrow-heads on the line $B'OB$. But the direction-cosines of OB are $(\sqrt{3}/2, \frac{1}{2})$ and those of OB' are $(-\sqrt{3}/2, -\frac{1}{2})$. Of course, the ratio $\sqrt{3}/2 : \frac{1}{2}$ is the same as the ratio $-\sqrt{3}/2 : -\frac{1}{2}$; and this ratio is generally written as $\sqrt{3} : 1$. A coordinate in our system is now not a single number, but a pair of numbers of which only the ratio matters. The coordinate of

OA is $(1:0)$, or $(2:0)$, or $(10:0)$, or $(-3\frac{1}{2}:0)$, etc.;

OB is $(\sqrt{3}:1)$, or $(3:\sqrt{3})$, etc.;

OC is $(1:1)$, etc.;

OD is $(0:1)$, etc.

Coordinates which, like these, are essentially ratios are called *homogeneous* coordinates, and are quite common in modern geometry. It very often happens, as here, that their main advantage is to include some exceptional element (here, the vertical line) which non-homogeneous coordinates did not include. (In geometry it is usually the so-called "point at infinity" or "line at infinity" which homogeneous coordinates bring into the system.) If we are interested only in the inclination of a line to the axes, and not in the actual position of the line, these homogeneous coordinates are useful. If we are considering the slope of the tangent at $(a, \phi\{a\})$ to the graph of ϕ then, provided that the slope is not vertical, its value is $\phi'(a)$. Then $\phi'(a)$ is the non-homogeneous coordinate of the direction of the tangent. In the dependent-variable notation (if $y = \phi(x)$), the coordinate is y_x. We denote the corresponding homogeneous coordinates by dy and dx. If y_x exists, dy and dx are any two numbers for which $dy/dx = y_x$. If the tangent is vertical, then $dx = 0$, and dy is any non-zero number.

We have not defined dy and dx separately, but have defined only their ratio. Every context in which we use them will be one in which only their ratio matters. Notice that we have defined them only for differentiable functions. dx and dy are *differentials* of x and y, respectively. The notation whereby dx is used as a single symbol (like a_1 or ϕ'), not the product of d with x, is admittedly unexpected; but it is well-established for historical reasons.

10.

Illustrations

(i) If $y = x^2$, then $dy = 2x \cdot dx$. In fact, dx and dy are any two variables for which $dy = 2x \cdot dx$.

(ii) If $\phi(x, y) = 0$, then

$$\phi_1(x, y) + \phi_2(x, y) \cdot y_x = 0;$$

and so

$$\phi_1(x, y) \cdot dx + \phi_2(x, y) \cdot dy = 0,$$

provided $dx \neq 0$. If $dx = 0$, then $x_y = 0$. But, in general,

$$\phi_1(x, y) \cdot x_y + \phi_2(x, y) = 0,$$

and so in this case $\phi_2(x, y) = 0$. Thus the formula

$$\phi_1(x, y) \cdot dx + \phi_2(x, y) \cdot dy = 0$$

is true in this case also.

(iii) If $x - y = \sin (x + y)$, then

$$dx - dy = \{\cos (x + y)\} \cdot (dx + dy).$$

If we are looking for local maxima and minima of y as x varies, the stationary values are those for which $dy = 0$: that is, $\cos (x + y) = 1$. If we are

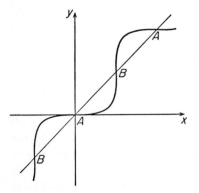

looking for local maxima and minima of x as y varies, the stationary values are those for which $dx = 0$: that is, $\cos (x + y) = -1$. Actually, the curve is a sine curve with its axis along $y = x$, and neither x nor y has a local maximum or minimum. All the stationary points are points of inflection.

(iv) If $x^2 + 4y^2 = 16$, then $2x \cdot dx + 8y \cdot dy = 0$. The points where the curve whose equation is $x^2 + 4y^2 = 16$ is horizontal are then given by $dy = 0$. Then $2x \cdot dx = 0$: that is, $x = 0$. Thus the points are $(0, 2)$ and $(0, -2)$. The points where it is vertical are given by $dx = 0$. Then $8y \cdot dy = 0$: that is, $y = 0$. Therefore, the points are $(4, 0)$ and $(-4, 0)$.

11.

It should be fairly clear that the main use of dx and dy is when x and y are two mutually related variables, rather than when x is a variable in its own right and y is dependent on x. Where the variables are on the same footing, it is convenient to use dy and dx, which are on the same footing. Where y explicitly depends on x, we should use y_x, and if x were explicitly to depend on y, we should use x_y.

12.

Problems

(i) Show that the direction-ratio at (a, b) of the curve $\phi(x, y) = 0$ is $-\phi_1(a, b) : \phi_2(a, b)$.

(ii) Find the points (if any) at which the tangents to the following curves are horizontal or vertical:

$$(y - 1)^2 = 4(x - 2);$$

$$x^2 + 3x \cdot y - y^2 = 9;$$

$$x \cdot y = 1;$$

$$a \cdot x^2 + 2h \cdot x \cdot y + b \cdot y^2 + 2g \cdot x + 2f \cdot y + c = 0;$$

$$\cos (x - y) = x + y.$$

13.

We have seen that we need to be careful in using the dependent-variable notation. A dependent variable is a function of some other variable, and can be *different* functions of different variables. Let us, then, consider carefully the following situation: u is a function of x which is a function of t:

$$u = \alpha(x); \quad x = \beta(t). \quad \text{Then}$$

$du = \alpha'(x) \cdot dx;$ and $dx = \beta'(t) \cdot dt.$ This tells us that

(i) $\qquad\qquad du = \alpha'\{\beta(t)\} \cdot \beta'(t) \cdot dt.$

But u is, of course, a function of t:

$$u = \alpha\{\beta(t)\},$$

and so du is defined directly in terms of t:

(ii) $\qquad\qquad du = \psi(t) \cdot dt,$

where $\psi(t)$ is the derivative of $\alpha\{\beta(t)\}$ re t. But the chain-rule tells us that

$$\psi(t) = \alpha'\{\beta(t)\} \cdot \beta'(t),$$

and so (ii) and (i) are the same. Thus the dependent-variable notation causes no ambiguity. Whether we regard u as a function of x or of t, du means the same thing. It is *only* because of this fact that the concept of differential is usable.

14.

Now let us turn to the case of more than two variables. We want to define their differentials when they are mutually related. Because, however, the situation is more complicated than that for two variables, we shall deal only with the case where one is an explicit function of the others, and we shall start with just three variables. Let us, then, consider a differentiable binary function ϕ and put

$$u = \phi(x, y).$$

We define du, dx, and dy to be any numbers for which

$$du = h_x \cdot dx + h_y \cdot dy.$$

Then u is stationary if, and only if, $du = 0$, and so on as before.

Notice that we have defined differentials only for differentiable functions. Why did we not define them for *any* function whose derivatives exist? The reason is that all, or nearly all, the useful properties of differentials are enjoyed by differentiable functions but not, in general, by functions that are less well-behaved.

15.

Problems

(i) If $x = r \cdot \cos t$ and $y = r \cdot \sin t$, find dx and dy in terms of r, t, dr, and dt.

(ii) If $r = (x^2 + y^2)^{1/2}$ and $t = \arctan(y/x)$, find dr and dt in terms of dx and dy.

(iii) Noticing that the transformations in (i) and (ii) are essentially the same (cartesians to and from polars in the region $x > 0$) check that the two sets of equations connecting the four differentials are essentially the same.

(iv) Prove that if $u = \phi(t^2, \sin t)$, where ϕ_1 and ϕ_2 are continuous,

$$\frac{du}{dt} = 2t \cdot \phi_1(t^2, \sin t) + \cos t \cdot \phi_2(t^2, \sin t),$$

(provided $dt \neq 0$).

16.

Again we must check that our dependent-variable notation does not lead to inconsistencies. Suppose that $u = \phi(x, y)$, where $x = \xi(t)$ and $y = \eta(t)$. Then

(i) $$du = \phi_1(x, y) \cdot dx + \phi_2(x, y) \cdot dy$$

by definition.

Also

$$u = \phi\{\xi(t),\, \eta(t)\},$$

and so

(ii)
$$du = \psi(t)\cdot dt,$$

where $\psi(t)$ is the derivative re t of $\phi\{\xi(t),\, \eta(t)\}$.

We have to check that (i) and (ii) are consistent with one another. This follows immediately from the chain-rule for differentiating

$$\phi\{\xi(t),\, \eta(t)\} \text{ re } t.$$

In other words,

$$du = u_x\cdot dx + u_y\cdot dy,$$

whether x and y are independent of one another, or related to one another.

17.

Clearly we can define differentials for ternary and higher functions in the same way, and check that

$$du = u_x\cdot dx + u_y\cdot dy + u_z\cdot dz + \ldots,$$

no matter how many (or how few) relations there are between $x,\, y,\, z,\, \ldots$.

Notice the happy resemblance between the equation

$$du = u_x\cdot dx + u_y\cdot dy$$

and the approximation

$$\Delta u \fallingdotseq u_x\cdot \Delta x + u_y\cdot \Delta y,$$

which we get by "translating" the formula for Δu into dependent-variable notation, and writing Δx and Δy for the quantities which we called h and k; namely, the increments in x and y. This inspires the phrase "differentials may be used to approximate to increments." Δu is the increment of u corresponding to increments Δx and Δy of x and of y.

18.

Problems

(i) $u = x + y + z;\ v = x\cdot y\cdot z$. Prove that

$$du = dx + dy + dz \quad \text{and} \quad dv = x\cdot y\cdot dz + x\cdot z\cdot dy + y\cdot z\cdot dx.$$

(ii) $x = r\cdot\sin s\cdot\cos t,\ y = r\cdot\sin s\cdot\sin t,\ z = r\cdot\cos s$. Find formulas for dx, dy, and dz in terms of r, s, t, dr, ds, and dt. Then find formulas for dr, ds, and dt in terms of x, y, z, dx, dy, and dz.

19.

Suppose that u depends on x and y; so that $u = \phi(x, y)$, say, and

(i)
$$du = \phi_1(x, y)\cdot dx + \phi_2(x, y)\cdot dy.$$

Can there be any other functions besides ϕ_1 and ϕ_2 for which a similar equation is true (for every x, y, dy, and dx)?

The answer is no. If

(ii) $$du = \alpha(x, y) \cdot dx + \beta(x, y) \cdot dy,$$

for every x, y, dy and dx, then $\alpha = \phi_1$ and $\beta = \phi_2$. To see this, we reflect that if (i) and (ii) are true for every x, y, dy, and dx, then the following is also true:

(iii) $$\alpha(x, y) \cdot dx + \beta(x, y) \cdot dy = \phi_1(x, y)\, dx + \phi_2(x, y) \cdot dy.$$

In particular, this will be true when $dy = 0$ and $dx = 1$. That is,

$$\alpha(x, y) = \phi_1(x, y) \quad \text{for every } x \text{ and } y.$$

Similarly

$$\beta(x, y) = \phi_2(x, y) \quad \text{for every } x \text{ and } y.$$

In practice we do not need to postulate that (ii) is true for *every* x, y, dx, and dy. As long as the values of dx (and also dy) for which it is true include 0 and at least one non-zero value, the above argument holds, and we reach the conclusion that

$$\alpha(x, y) = \phi_1(x, y) \quad \text{for every relevant } x \text{ and } y.$$

For example, if

$$u = \log_e (x + y)$$

and

$$du = \alpha(x, y) \cdot dx + \beta(x, y) \cdot dy,$$

for every dx and dy less than $\frac{1}{1000}$ in absolute value, and for every x and y for which $x + y$ is positive, then

$$\alpha(x, y) = \beta(x, y) = (x + y)^{-1}$$

for every x and y for which $x + y$ is positive. In this case we could not say "for every x and y"; because neither $\log_e (x + y)$ nor $(x + y)^{-1}$ is defined when $x + y = 0$.

20.

Let us investigate one way in which we can use the result of **19**. Suppose that we have a variable whose value at the point (x, y) in a system of cartesian coordinates, is given by

$$w = x/y + 1,$$

and suppose that the cartesian system is related to a polar system by

$$x = r \cdot \cos t, \qquad y = r \cdot \sin t,$$

and that the polar system is related to yet a third system by

$$r = u \cdot (e^v - e^{-v}), \qquad t = u \cdot (e^v + e^{-v}).$$

Let us find the derivatives of w re u and v. We can find the derivatives of w re x and y easily enough. To get the derivatives of w re r and t we could use the chain-rule, and then using the chain-rule again will give us the derivatives re u and v. But we have seen that it was precisely the chain-rule which justified the notation of differentials. Thus, using differentials is essentially equivalent to using the chain-rule. We might expect, then, that simply by writing down differentials we could obtain the required result. This is indeed true, and this method is probably the simplest way of getting it. In this case:

$$dw = \frac{1}{y} \cdot dx - \frac{x}{y^2} \cdot dy,$$

$$dx = dr \cdot \cos t - dt \cdot r \cdot \sin t,$$

$$dy = dr \cdot \sin t + dt \cdot r \cdot \cos t.$$

Therefore

$$dw = \frac{1}{r \cdot \sin t} \left(dr \cdot \cos t - dt \cdot r \cdot \sin t \right) - \frac{\cos t}{r \cdot \sin^2 t} \left(dr \cdot \sin t + dt \cdot r \cdot \cos t \right)$$

$$= 0 \cdot dr - (\cot^2 t + 1) \cdot dt = -\csc^2 t \cdot dt.$$

Again

$$dt = du \cdot (e^v + e^{-v}) + dv \cdot u \cdot (e^v - e^{-v}).$$

Therefore

$$dw = -\csc^2 \{ u \cdot (e^v + e^{-v}) \} \cdot \{ du \cdot (e^v + e^{-v}) + dv \cdot u \cdot (e^v - e^{-v}) \}.$$

This gives

$$w_u = -\csc^2 \{ u \cdot (e^v + e^{-v}) \} \cdot (e^v + e^{-v}),$$

and $\qquad w_v = -\csc^2 \{ u \cdot (e^v + e^{-v}) \} \cdot u \cdot (e^v - e^{-v}).$

Other problems which have been solved by the chain-rule can also be done (often a little quicker) using differentials.

Illustrative problem. Variables x and y are functions of u and v and, at the same time, u and v are functions of x and y. Find u_x in terms of x_u, x_v, y_u, and y_v.

A solution:

$$dx = x_u \cdot du + x_v \cdot dv$$

$$dy = y_u \cdot du + y_v \cdot dv.$$

Therefore, solving for du,

$$-y_v \cdot dx + x_v \cdot dy = (-x_u \cdot y_v + y_u \cdot x_v) \cdot du.$$

Then, if $x_u \cdot y_v \neq x_v \cdot y_u$,

$$du = \frac{y_v}{x_u \cdot y_v - y_u \cdot x_v} \cdot dx + \frac{x_v}{y_u \cdot x_v - x_u \cdot y_v} \cdot dy.$$

Therefore

$$u_x = y_v/(x_u \cdot y_v - y_u \cdot x_v),$$

provided that the denominator is not zero. Formulas for u_y, v_x, and v_y can be found similarly.

Note. this is really the same problem as in **D15**.

21

Problems

(i) $x = e^u \cdot \ln v$ and $y = e^v \cdot \ln u$. Find a formula for u_x.

(ii) u, v, and w are connected by an equation which is (locally) solvable for u as a function of v and w. The (partial) derivative of u re v is required. Show that it can be found as follows: Write down the differential of the equation between u, v, and w (for example, if the equation is $u^2 + v = w$, write $2u \cdot du + dv = dw$), put $dw = 0$, and solve for du/dv. Then du/dv is the required derivative.

(iii) Find as in (ii) the mutual derivatives of u, v and w if $u^2 + v^2 + w^2 = 0$. Find the derivatives if

$$\left(u + \frac{1}{v^2}\right) \cdot (v - 2) = 3w.$$

(iv) Five variables p, v, t, s, u are such that any two may be chosen and the others regarded as functions of them. All functions involved have continuous derivatives up to the second order, and the variables satisfy the equation

$$t \cdot ds = du + p \cdot dv.$$

$(s_v)_t$ denotes the derivative of s re v when s is regarded as a function of v and t. Prove that

$$(s_v)_t = (p_t)_v \quad \text{and} \quad (v_s)_p = (t_p)_s.$$

22.

Given a dependent variable, we can usually write down its differential. If u is $x^2 + x \cdot y$, then its differential is

$$(2x + y) \cdot dx + x \cdot dy.$$

Let us consider the opposite problem: Given an expression of the form

$$h \cdot dx + k \cdot dy,$$

where h and k depend on x and y, find an expression of which it is the differential. Let us suppose, for example, that we are given the following equation.

(i) $\qquad\qquad du = (2x - y) \cdot dx + (2y - x) \cdot dy.$

Because du is

$$u_x \cdot dx + u_x \cdot dy,$$

solving (i) amounts to finding a u for which

$$u_x = 2x - y \quad \text{and} \quad u_y = 2y - x.$$

Now

$$(x^2 - x \cdot y)_x = 2x - y;$$

and so $x^2 - x \cdot y$ has the desired x-derivative. In fact, if u is as desired, $(u - x^2 + x \cdot y)_x = 0$, and so $u - x^2 + x \cdot y$ is independent of x:

$$u = x^2 - x \cdot y + g,$$

say, where g depends on y only. Then

$$u_y = -x + g_y.$$

But we require $u_y = 2y - x$. This will be true if, and only if, $g_y = 2y$, and this in turn will be true if, and only if, $g = y^2 + a$ for some number a. Then

$$u = x^2 - x \cdot y + y^2 + a.$$

This is the solution of (i) for u.

Let us consider another example:

(ii) $$du = (2x - y) \cdot dx + (2y + x) \cdot dy.$$

As before, if u satisfies this, then

$$u_y = -x + g_y$$

where g depends on y only. But now we require $u_y = x + 2y$. That is, we require

$$-x + g_y = x + 2y$$

where g depends on y only. This is clearly impossible. Thus (ii) has no solution for u.

An expression which is equal to a differential is called an *exact differential*. We say that the right-hand side of (i) is an exact differential, and that of (ii) is not.

23.

There is an easy way to tell whether a given expression is an exact differential or not as long as we restrict ourselves to differentiable functions.

If $h \cdot dx + k \cdot dy$ is equal to du, say, then $h = u_x$ and $k = u_y$. Then $h_y = u_{xy}$ and $k_x = u_{yx}$. Now it follows from **B7** that $u_{xy} = u_{yx}$. Thus $h_y = k_x$.

Then we have the rule which states that to test $h \cdot dx + k \cdot dy$ for exactness, see whether $h_y = k_x$. If not, then $h \cdot dx + k \cdot dy$ is not exact. Conversely, if h_y does equal k_x, then $h \cdot dx + k \cdot dy$ is exact.

To see this, let h be $\alpha(x, y)$ and k be $\beta(x, y)$. Then $\alpha_2 = \beta_1$. Define a variable u by

$$u = \phi(x, y) + \int_{t=0}^{y} \beta(0, t) \cdot dt,$$

where $\phi(x, y) = \int_{t=0}^{x} \alpha(t, y) \cdot dt$.

Then u will be a variable whose differential is $h \cdot dx + k \cdot dy$. To prove this, we find u_x and u_y. Now,

$$\phi_1(x, y) = \alpha(x, y) = h.$$

Also, $\phi(0, y) = 0$, and so $\phi_2(0, y) = 0$. Then

$$\phi_2(x, y) = \phi_2(x, y) - \phi_2(0, y)$$

$$= \int_{t=0}^{x} \phi_{21}(t, y) \cdot dt$$

$$= \int_{t=0}^{x} \phi_{12}(t, y) \cdot dt$$

$$= \int_{t=0}^{x} \alpha_2(t, y) \cdot dt$$

$$= \int_{t=0}^{x} \beta_1(t, y) \cdot dt$$

$$= \beta(x, y) - \beta(0, y).$$

Therefore,

$$u_x = \phi_1(x, y) = h$$

and

$$u_y = \phi_2(x, y) + \beta(0, y) = \beta(x, y) = k.$$

Now we are supposing that the functions which h and k are of x and y are differentiable; therefore they are continuous. The function which u is of x and y has continuous derivatives, and so is differentiable. Thus u has a differential, and it equals $h \cdot dx + k \cdot dy$.

24.

Problems

(i) Find a u (if possible) for which

$$du = (2x \cdot y - y^2 + 2x) \cdot dx + (x^2 - 2x \cdot y + 2y) \cdot dy.$$

(ii) Find a u (if possible) for which

$$du = y \cdot (y^2 + 3x^2) \cdot dy + x \cdot (x^2 + 3y^2) \cdot dx.$$

(iii) Find a u (if possible) for which

$$du = 2 \cdot \sin x \cdot \cos x \cdot \sin (x + y) \cdot dx + \sin^2 x \cdot \cos (x + y) \cdot (dx + dy).$$

(iv) Find a u (if possible) for which

$$du = (1 - x^2) \cdot dy + (x \cdot y - x) \cdot dx.$$

(v) Find a relation between x and y which will ensure that
$$(3x^2 \cdot y^2 + 2x \cdot y^2) \cdot dx + (2x^3 \cdot y + 2x^2 \cdot y) \cdot dy = 0.$$
Find all such relations.

(vi) Find a relation between x and y which will ensure that
$$x + y + (x + y^2) \cdot y_x = 0.$$

(vii) Solve the equation
$$\frac{x}{y^2} \cdot y_x = x + \frac{1}{y}.$$

(viii) Solve the equation
$$x \cdot dy - y \cdot dx + x^3 \cdot dx = 0$$

J

Taylor's Theorem

1.

Let us recall Taylor's theorem for singulary functions: If $\phi^{(n)}(x)$ exists whenever $a \leqslant x \leqslant a + h$, there is a t between 0 and 1 for which

(i) $$\phi(a + h) = \sum_{r=0}^{n-1} h^r \cdot \phi^{(r)}(a)/r! + h^n \cdot \phi^{(n)}(a + t \cdot h)/n!$$

The formula can be proved to hold under somewhat weaker assumptions, but the above form of the theorem is suitable for our purposes.*

A similar theorem holds for m-ary functions. For simplicity, let us first consider a binary function ψ. We want a formula analogous to (i) for $\psi(a + h, b + k)$. Let us suppose that the derivatives of ψ up to the

---

* A proof will be found in H. A. Thurston, *Differentiation and Integration*, Blackie, 1961, p. 60, and many other textbooks of the calculus.

$(n-1)$th order obey the chain-rule. Define a singulary ϕ by

$$\phi(t) = \psi(a + h{\cdot}t,\, b + k{\cdot}t).$$

Then

(ii) $\qquad \phi'(t) = h{\cdot}\psi_1(a + h{\cdot}t,\, b + k{\cdot}t) + k{\cdot}\psi_2(a + h{\cdot}t,\, b + k{\cdot}t),$

and we can find $\phi''(t)$ similarly. A general formula for $\phi^{(r)}(t)$ is not easy to write down. To simplify it, we define an "operator" $\mathfrak{D}_{h,k}$ as follows:

If θ is any binary function for which θ_1 and θ_2 exist, then $\mathfrak{D}_{h,k}\theta$ is the binary function for which

$$\mathfrak{D}_{h,k}\theta(x, y) = h{\cdot}\theta_1(x, y) + k{\cdot}\theta_2(x, y).$$

Naturally, $\mathfrak{D}_{h,k}^2\theta$ denotes $\mathfrak{D}_{h,k}(\mathfrak{D}_{h,k}\theta)$, and so on.

Now (ii) becomes

$$\phi'(t) = \mathfrak{D}_{h,k}\psi(a + h{\cdot}t,\, b + k{\cdot}t),$$

and, in general,

(iii) $\qquad \phi^{(r)}(t) = \mathfrak{D}_{h,k}^r\psi(a + h{\cdot}t,\, b + k{\cdot}t).$

Formula (i), with 0 in place of a and 1 in place of h, yields

$$\phi(1) = \sum_{r=0}^{n-1} \phi^{(r)}(0)/r! + \phi^{(n)}(t)/n!$$

for some t between 0 and 1, which gives, by (iii),

(iv) $\qquad \psi(a + h,\, b + k) = \sum_{r=0}^{n-1} \mathfrak{D}_{h,k}^r\psi(a, b)/r!$

$$+ \mathfrak{D}_{h,k}^n\psi(a + h{\cdot}t,\, b + k{\cdot}t)/n!$$

for some t between 0 and 1. This is the required formula. There are similar ones for ternary and higher functions.

A less compact but more common and more explicit formula is obtained by using

$$\left(h \cdot \frac{\partial}{\partial x} + k \cdot \frac{\partial}{\partial y}\right),$$

in place of $\mathfrak{D}_{h,k}$. Then, if we write f for $\psi(x, y)$,

$$\Delta f = \sum_{r=1}^{n-1}\left(\Delta x \cdot \frac{\partial}{\partial x} + \Delta y \cdot \frac{\partial}{\partial y}\right)^r\!\! f \Big/ r! + \left\{\left(\Delta x \cdot \frac{\partial}{\partial x} + \Delta y \frac{\partial}{\partial y}\right)^n\!\! f\right\}^* \Big/ n!$$

where the asterisk denotes that the variable in the braces is evaluated at

$$(x + t{\cdot}\Delta x,\, y + t{\cdot}\Delta y),$$

for some t between 0 and 1.

Note. Our proof requires that the derivatives of orders up to the $(n-1)$th satisfy the chain-rule, and we have used the rule only at pairs of the form

$$(a + h{\cdot}t,\, b + k{\cdot}t) \quad \text{for} \quad 0 \leqslant t \leqslant 1.$$

The only other condition is that ψ has to be well enough behaved for $\phi^{(n)}(t)$ to exist whenever $0 \leqslant t \leqslant 1$. Hence, sufficient conditions for the theorem to be true are: (a) The derivatives of ψ up to the nth order are continuous at all such pairs, or (b) The derivatives of ψ up to the $(n-1)$th order are differentiable at all such pairs.

2.

Problems

　(i) Write out the formula (iv) when $a = b = 0$ in the cases $n = 1$ and $n = 2$, without using the abbreviation $\mathfrak{D}_{h,k}$.

　(ii) Write out in full $\mathfrak{D}_{h,k}^5 \theta(a, b)$. Compare with the expansion of $(u + v)^5$. (Assume that the 5th-order derivatives of θ are continuous.)

　(iii) Write out the formula (iv) in the case

$$n = 3, \psi(x, y) = x \cdot \sin y + y \cdot \cos x.$$

　(iv) Prove that, given x and y, neither zero, there is a t between 0 and 1 for which

$$\frac{\sin x}{x} + \frac{\sin y}{y} = \frac{\sin (x \cdot t)}{x} + \frac{\sin (y \cdot t)}{y} + t \cdot \{\cos (x \cdot t) + \cos (y \cdot t)\}.$$

Hint: Consider ψ where $\psi(x, y) = x \cdot \sin y + y \cdot \sin x$.

　(v) Prove that, given x and y, neither zero, there is a t between 0 and 1 for which

$$\frac{\sin x}{x} + \frac{\sin y}{y} = \cos (x \cdot t) + \cos (y \cdot t) - \frac{t}{2} \cdot \{x \cdot \sin (x \cdot t) + y \cdot \sin (y \cdot t)\}.$$

Maxima and Minima

1.

We recall that if $\phi'(a) = 0$, ϕ is said to be stationary at a; and we also recall that, in general, local maxima and minima of ϕ occur where ϕ is stationary. More precisely, if ϕ has a local maximum or minimum at a, then *either* $\phi'(a) = 0$, *or* $\phi'(a)$ does not exist.

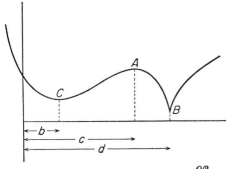

A: local maximum, $\phi'(c) = 0$
B: local minimum,
      $\phi'(d)$ does not exist
C: local minimum, $\phi'(b) = 0$

2.

Let us call numbers a for which $\phi'(a) = 0$, or $\phi'(a)$ fails to exist, *critical numbers* for ϕ. A critical number need not yield a local maximum or minimum, but a local maximum or minimum cannot occur except at a critical number. If we want to find local maxima or minima of ϕ, we differentiate ϕ and so find its critical numbers. We then investigate each critical number. So much is familiar. Now we can do the same for binary functions. We define ψ to be *stationary* at (a, b) if $\psi_1(a, b) = \psi_2(a, b) = 0$. We say that (a, b) is *critical* for ψ if ψ is stationary at (a, b), or if either of the two derivatives fails to exist there. Then to find all local maxima and minima of ψ we differentiate ψ and find the critical pairs. Among them are all the local maxima and minima.

We can see this as follows. Suppose that ψ has a local maximum at (a, b). Introduce a singulary θ by putting

$$\theta(x) = \psi(x, b).$$

Then, as in **B2**, $\theta'(a) = \psi_1(a, b)$, and the one exists if, and only if, the other does. Now $\psi(a, b) \geqslant \psi(x, y)$ for every (x, y) near enough to (a, b). Therefore $\psi(a, b) \geqslant \psi(x, b)$ for every x near enough to a. That is, $\theta(a) \geqslant \theta(x)$ for every x near enough to a, which means that θ has a local maximum at a. Then $\theta'(a)$, if it exists, must be zero, whence $\psi_1(a, b)$, if it exists, is zero. Similarly, $\psi_2(a, b)$, if it exists, must be zero. Thus *either* they are both zero, *or* one of them fails to exist. In either case, (a, b) is critical for ψ.

Similar definitions hold for a local minimum and for functions of more variables.

3.

Now let us re-work the calculation of the illustrative problem **A4** in this notation. The expression whose minimum we require is $4/y + 8/x + 2x \cdot y$, where x and y are positive.

Let

$$\theta(x, y) = 4/y + 8/x + 2x \cdot y.$$

Then

$$\theta_1(x, y) = -8/x^2 + 2y,$$

and

$$\theta_2(x, y) = -4/y^2 + 2x.$$

$\theta_1(x, y)$ and $\theta_2(x, y)$ are both zero if, and only if, $x^2 \cdot y = 4$ and $x \cdot y^2 = 2$. In other words, $x = 2$ and $y = 1$. We have now found the one and only stationary pair, which is the only critical pair.

4.

Problems

(i) Find the local maxima and minima, if any, of

$$x^2 + 4y^2 - 2x; \sin u + \sin v + \sin (u + v);$$
$$a \cdot b + 1/a + 1/b; \quad x \cdot y; \quad u^3 + v^3 - 3u \cdot v;$$
$$x^2 + y^2 + z^2 + 2x + 4y - 2z.$$

(ii) $OABC$ is a tetrahedral piece of wood. Angles AOB, BOC and COA are all right angles. $OA = 3$ cm, $OB = 6$ cm, and $OC = 9$ cm. A rectangular solid is to be cut out of it, with O as one vertex. Find the biggest such solid.

(iii) Find the equation of the plane through (1, 2, 1) which cuts off the least volume from the first octant. (The first octant is that part of space in which all three coordinates are positive.)

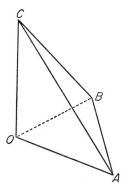

5.

Let us suppose that we are looking for local maxima and minima of a binary function ϕ by investigating its critical pairs. In fact, let

$$\phi_1(a, b) = \phi_2(a, b) = 0.$$

Let ϕ_{11}, ϕ_{12}, ϕ_{21}, and ϕ_{22} be continuous at all points in some circle about (a, b) and have values l, m and n, respectively, at (a, b). Then we have the following test for the behavior of ϕ at (a, b). (i) ϕ has a local extremum at (a, b) if $l \cdot n - m^2 > 0$; (ii) ϕ has no local extremum at (a, b) if $l \cdot n - m^2 < 0$. Moreover, in the first case, the extremum is a maximum if $l < 0$, a minimum if $l > 0$. This part of the test is the same as the "second-order-derivative test" used for singulary functions. The second case, which tells us that there is no local extremum, has no counterpart for singulary functions. The proof is postponed until **M19**. If $l \cdot n - m^2 = 0$, there may or may not be a local extremum, as we can see by considering $a = 0, b = 0$, and $\phi(x, y) = x^4 + y^4$, or $-x^4 - y^4$, or $x^4 - y^4$, all of which yield $l \cdot n - m^2 = 0$, but which have, respectively, a local minimum, a local maximum, and no local extremum.

6.

Illustrative problem. To find the local maxima and minima of

$$4/y + 8/x + 2x \cdot y.$$

(This is the same expression as in **A4**). Call the expression $\theta(x, y)$. Then

$$\theta_1(x, y) = \theta_2(x, y) = 0$$

if, and only if, $(x, y) = (2, 1)$, as in **A5**. We must now investigate the critical pair $(2, 1)$.

$$\theta_{11}(2, 1) = 16/8 = 2$$
$$\theta_{12}(2, 1) = 2$$
$$\theta_{22}(2, 1) = 8/1 = 8.$$

Then

$$\theta_{11}(2, 1) \cdot \theta_{22}(2, 1) - \theta_{12}(2, 1)^2 = 16 - 4 > 0;$$

and so we have a local extremum. $\theta_{11}(2, 1) > 0$, which means that the extremum is a minimum.

7.

Problems. Find the stationary pairs for ϕ where

(i) $\phi(x, y) = x^2 - x \cdot y + y^2$ for every x and y;

(ii) $\phi(x, y) = \sin x + \sin y + \sin (x + y)$ for every x and y;

(iii) $\phi(x, y) = x^{-1} + x \cdot y - 8y^{-1}$ for every non-zero x and y.

Which pairs give local maxima and minima?

(iv) Find the point on the plane $x + y - 2z + 1 = 0$ which is nearest the origin.

(v) Show that as t varies, the point

$$(\tfrac{1}{2}t, 3 - t, 1 + t)$$

traces out a straight line, and the point

$$(t - 1, -t, 4 + 3t)$$

traces another. Find the least distance between two points, one on each line.

8.

For finding greatest and least values of a function, local maxima and minima are useful. Let us recall the situation for singulary functions; suppose that we require the greatest value of $\phi(x)$ where x ranges from a to b, inclusive.

Let us investigate the conditions under which c can be the number at which ϕ has its greatest value. First, c may be a or b. If not, then there is

a range of possible values of x around c. Whenever x is in this range, $\phi(c) \geqslant \phi(x)$, because $\phi(c)$ is the greatest value of ϕ. Then c gives a local maximum of ϕ. Thus the greatest value of ϕ *either* occurs at a or b, the end-points of the possible values of the argument-variable; *or* is a local maximum.

The same thing applies to binary functions. Suppose that we want the greatest value of $\psi(x, y)$ for (x, y) in a certain set D. The greatest value *either* is a local maximum, *or* occurs at a pair on the boundary of D; that is, at a pair such that not every pair near it is in D.

9.

Illustrative problem. The concentration of fertilizer at a point distant x meters from the west edge and y meters from the south edge of a square field whose edges run N–S and E–W and are 100 meters long is

$$1000 + x + y - \tfrac{1}{10}x \cdot y \quad \text{units.}$$

At what point of the field is the concentration greatest?

A solution. Let

$$\phi(x, y) = 1000 + x + y - \tfrac{1}{10} \cdot x \cdot y,$$

so that ϕ has continuous derivatives: in fact,

$$\phi_1(x, y) = 1 - \tfrac{1}{10}y, \quad \text{and} \quad \phi_2(x, y) = 1 - \tfrac{1}{10}x.$$

The only critical pair for ϕ is $(10, 10)$, and

$$\phi(10, 10) = 1,010.$$

Consider the west edge: $\phi(0, y) = 1000 + y$, and its greatest value (for values of (x, y) under consideration) is 1100 when $y = 100$.

The east edge is similar:

$$\phi(100, y) = 1100 - 9y,$$

and the greatest value on this edge is:

$$\phi(100, 0) = 1100.$$

The south edge gives:

$$\phi(x, 0) = 1000 + x,$$

and the greatest value on this edge is:

$$\phi(100, 0) = 1100.$$

The north edge gives:

$$\phi(x, 100) = 1100 - 9x,$$

and the greatest value on this edge is

$$\phi(0, 100) = 1100.$$

These are the only possibilities for the greatest value in the field; thus the value required is the greatest of these; namely, 1100. It occurs at two points, $(0, 100)$ and $(100, 0)$, which are the north-west and south-east corners, respectively.

We could look for the least value in the same way. The possibilities are:

In the interior of the field: $\phi(10, 10) = 1010$.
On the west edge: $\phi(0, 0) = 1000$.
On the east edge: $\phi(100, 100) = 200$.
On the south edge: $\phi(0, 0) = 1000$.
On the north edge: $\phi(100, 100) = 200$.

The least value is, therefore, 200 and occurs at the north-east corner.

10.

Illustrative problem. Find the least distance from the origin to the surface $x^2 - z^2 = 1$.

A solution. The square of the distance required will be least when the distance is least. We want, in this case, the least value of

$$x^2 + y^2 + z^2, \quad \text{when} \quad x^2 - z^2 = 1.$$

In other words, we want the least value of

$$2x^2 - 1 + y^2, \quad \text{when} \quad x^2 - z^2 = 1.$$

What are the possible values of x and y? We know that $x^2 = 1 + z^2$, and, therefore, that $x^2 \geqslant 1$. Either $x \geqslant 1$ or $x \leqslant -1$, and y is unrestricted. Conversely, given *any* x for which $x^2 \geqslant 1$ and *any* y, there is a z for which (x, y, z) is on the surface $x^2 - z^2 = 1$, the z in question being $(x^2 - 1)^{1/2}$. Thus the range of (x, y) to be considered is

$$\begin{cases} x \geqslant 1 \quad \text{or} \quad x \leqslant 1 \\ y \quad \text{unrestricted.} \end{cases}$$

On the diagram it is represented as the shaded region. The derivatives of $2x^2 - 1 + y^2$ are $4x$ and $2y$. There is no pair in the range we are considering

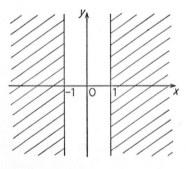

which would make them both zero, because x is never zero in our range, and so the first derivative is never zero in the range. Thus we have no critical pairs and so no *local* minimum. The boundary is given by $x = 1$, in which case we want the least value of $1 + y^2$, and by $x = -1$, in which case we also want the least value of $1 + y^2$. These occur when $y = 0$. Thus the least distance is 1. The points on the surface at this distance from the origin are given by $x = 1$, $y = 0$, and $x = -1$, $y = 0$, so they are the points $(1, 0, 0)$ and $(-1, 0, 0)$.

Another solution. We want the least value of

$$x^2 + y^2 + z^2, \quad \text{when} \quad x^2 - z^2 = 1.$$

That is, we want the least value of

$$1 + y^2 + 2z^2, \quad \text{when} \quad x^2 - z^2 = 1.$$

What are the possible values of y and z? They are unrestricted. Take *any* y and *any* z and make $x = (1 + z^2)^{1/2}$, and then (x, y, z) lies on the surface $x^2 - z^2 = 1$.

Clearly, the least value of $1 + y^2 + 2z^2$ is 1, when $y = z = 0$, so that we get the same answer as before. If the least value of $1 + y^2 + 2z^2$ had not been obvious, we should have gone on to look for local minima, and taken the least of these.

11.

The foregoing is a typical example of "conditional maxima and minima." We want not simply the least value of $x^2 + y^2 + z^2$, but the least value under the condition $x^2 - z^2 = 1$. The obvious technique (there are others) is to use the condition to eliminate one variable. We then have an ordinary maximum-and-minimum problem with one variable fewer, and no conditions between the variables. We cannot, however, just ignore the condition once we have used it to eliminate a variable: it might put a restriction on the possible values of the remaining variables and, in the first solution above, it did so. Theoretically, it does not matter which variable we eliminate. In practice, the details of the calculation can depend greatly on which one is chosen, and it is worth while looking ahead to see which gives the simplest working.

12.

Problems

(i) Find the greatest and least values of

$$x^2 + 2x \cdot y + 2y^2 - 3x,$$

when x ranges from 0 to 4, and y from -2 to 1, inclusive.

(ii) Find the greatest and least values of

$$x + y - x \cdot y$$

under the restrictions $x \geqslant 0$, $y \leqslant 2$, $x - y \leqslant 2$.

(iii) The temperature at the point (x, y) on the disc $x^2 + y^2 \leqslant 1$ is

$$(x^2 + 2y^2 - x) \, °\text{C}.$$

Find the hottest and coolest points on the disc.

(iv) Find the greatest and least values (if any) of $x + y + z$ under the condition

$$1/x + 4/y + 9/z = 1.$$

(v) Find the points on the curve of intersection of

$$x - y + 2z = 0 \quad \text{with} \quad x^2 + \tfrac{1}{4}y^2 + z^2 = 1,$$

which are nearest to the origin.

Simple Differential Equations

1.

Let us try to discover what functions θ satisfy the condition

(i) $\qquad\qquad \theta_1(x, y) = 0$ for every x and y.

If we put, for each y,

$$\phi(x) = \theta(x, y) \quad \text{for every } x,$$

then

$$\phi'(x) = \theta_1(x, y)$$

so that (i) is true if, and only if, for each y

$$\phi'(x) = 0 \quad \text{for every } x.$$

The functions ϕ which satisfy this are the constants. Therefore, ϕ satisfies this if, and only if, there is a number a such that $\phi(x) = a$ for every x; that is, $\theta(x, y) = a$ for every x.

To sum up: θ satisfies (i) if, and only if, for each y there is an a such that $\theta(x, y) = a$ for every x. The a here will depend on y, say $a = \alpha(y)$. Then we see that (i) is satisfied if, and only if, there is a singulary function α such that $\theta(x, y) = \alpha(y)$, for every x and y.

Another way of saying this is "θ satisfies (i) if, and only if, it is independent of its first argument."

Again, we say that $\theta(x, y) = \alpha(y)$ is a "solution" of the equation (i). Any function α will do. For example, $\theta(x, y) = \sin y$ will be a solution,

$$\theta(x, y) = y \cdot \sin y + e^y$$

will be a solution, and so on.

2.

Similarly,
$$\theta(x, y) = \beta(x)$$
is a solution of
$$\theta_2(x, y) = 0.$$
Again,
$$h = \alpha(y)$$
is a solution of
$$h_x = 0,$$
and
$$h = \beta(x)$$
is a solution of
$$h_y = 0.$$

All this agrees with the common-sense idea that if the rate-of-change of a quantity is zero, then the quantity does not change.

3.

Now let us solve for θ the equation

(i) $$\theta_1(x, y) = \theta_2(x, y) \quad \text{for every } x \text{ and } y.$$

We can reduce this to an equation of the type which we dealt with in **2**, by what amounts to a change of variables. Let us define ϕ by

$$\phi(u, v) = \theta\{\tfrac{1}{2}(u + v), \tfrac{1}{2}(u - v)\} \quad \text{for every } u \text{ and } v.$$

Then, $\theta(x, y) = \phi(x + y, x - y)$, for every x and y because, given any x and y, we can put

$$u = x + y \quad \text{and} \quad v = x - y,$$

whence $x = \tfrac{1}{2}(u + v)$ and $y = \tfrac{1}{2}(u - v)$.

Then, if θ is differentiable

$$\theta_1(x, y) = \phi_1(x + y, x - y) + \phi_2(x + y, x - y),$$

and

$$\theta_2(x, y) = \phi_1(x + y, x - y) - \phi_2(x + y, x - y).$$

Then (i) becomes

$$\phi_2(x + y, x - y) = 0 \quad \text{for every } x \text{ and } y.$$

We know that the solution of this is

$$\phi(x + y, x - y) = \alpha(x + y),$$

and so the solution of (i) is

$$\theta(x, y) = \alpha(x + y).$$

Because $\theta_1(x, y)$ and $\theta_2(x, y)$ exist for every x and y, α must be differentiable, but this is the only restriction on it. For example, $\theta(x, y) = (x + y)^2$ will be a solution, and so will

$$\theta(x, y) = (x + y) \cdot \sin (x + y) + e^{(x+y)};$$

4.

Let us repeat this in the dependent-variable notation, which is suitable for this kind of work if carefully used. We have to solve

$$h_x = h_y$$

for h. Put $u = x + y$ and $v = x - y$. Then the equation becomes

$$h_u \cdot u_x + h_v \cdot v_x = h_u \cdot u_y + h_v \cdot v_y.$$

That is,

$$h_u + h_v = h_u - h_v,$$

that is,

$$h_v = 0$$

whose solution is

$$h = \alpha(u),$$

that is,

$$h = \alpha(x + y).$$

We are, in effect, using a "change of variables" from (x, y) to (u, v). We can, of course, make similar changes for ternary functions. For example, to solve $h_x + h_z = 0$ put

$$\begin{cases} u = x - z \\ v = y \\ w = x + z. \end{cases}$$

Then

$$h_x = h_u + h_w$$

$$h_y = h_v,$$

and

$$h_z = -h_u + h_w.$$

Thus

$$h_x + h_z = 2h_w,$$

and our equation becomes $2h_w = 0$. The solution is $h = \phi(u, v)$; that is,

$$h = \phi(x - z, y),$$

for some ϕ.

The same substitution enables us to solve $h_x - h_z = 0$.

Notice that it would *not* do to write

$$\begin{cases} u = x - z \\ w = x + z, \end{cases}$$

and leave y unaltered. The two sets of variables would not be distinct, and we have seen that, in this case, the dependent-variable notation is liable to be ambiguous.

5.

Problems

(i) Prove that if

$$\phi(x, y) = \sin(a \cdot x + b \cdot y) \quad \text{for every } x \text{ and } y$$

then (a)

$$b \cdot \phi_1(x, y) = a \cdot \phi_2(x, y) \quad \text{for every } x \text{ and } y.$$

Prove that, if in place of sin we have any differentiable singulary function, then (a) still holds. In other words, prove that if ψ is differentiable and

$$\phi(x, y) = \psi(a \cdot x + b \cdot y) \quad \text{for every } x \text{ and } y,$$

then (a) is true.

(ii) Prove that if h is a function of x and y, a is a number, and

$$h = \phi(y - a \cdot x, y + a \cdot x) \quad \text{for every } x \text{ and } y,$$

then

$$h_x = a \cdot h_y \quad \text{for some } x \text{ and } y$$

if, and only if,

$$a \cdot \phi_1(y - a \cdot x, y + a \cdot x) = 0$$

for that x and y (assuming that h_x and h_y are continuous functions of x and y).

Prove that if $a \neq 0$, the equation

$$h_x = a \cdot h_y$$

has for solution

$$h = \alpha(y + a \cdot x),$$

for some singulary function α.

(iii) Prove that $\theta_1(x, y) = 2\theta_2(x, y)$ for every x and y if, and only if,

$$\theta(x, y) = \psi(x + 2y),$$

for some differentiable singulary ψ. (Assume that θ is differentiable.)

(iv) Solve the equation

$$a \cdot \phi_1(x, y) = b \cdot \phi_2(x, y)$$

for ϕ.

(v) Solve the equation

$$\phi_1(x, y, z) + \phi_2(x, y, z) = \phi_3(x, y, z)$$

for ϕ.

(vi) Solve the equation

$$u \cdot \phi_1(u, v) + v \cdot \phi_2(u, v) = 0$$

for ϕ. (Assume that ϕ is differentiable.)

6.

Let us investigate a partial differential equation which happens to be of particular interest in physics. For a given non-zero a,

(i) $\phi_{22}(x, t) = a^2 \cdot \phi_{11}(x, t)$ for every x and t.

To solve this, we shall use the dependent-variable notation. Let

$$u = x - a \cdot t, \quad v = x + a \cdot t \quad \text{and} \quad h = \phi(x, t).$$

Equation (i) becomes

(ii) $$h_{tt} = a^2 \cdot h_{xx}.$$

By the chain-rule,

$$h_t = h_u \cdot u_t + h_v \cdot v_t = -a \cdot h_u + a \cdot h_v,$$

whence

$$\begin{aligned}
h_{tt} &= h_{tu} \cdot u_t + h_{tv} \cdot v_t \\
&= -a \cdot (-a \cdot h_{uu} + a \cdot h_{vu}) + a \cdot (-a \cdot h_{uv} + a \cdot h_{vv}) \\
&= a^2 \cdot h_{uu} - a^2 \cdot h_{vu} - a^2 \cdot h_{uv} + a^2 \cdot h_{vv}.
\end{aligned}$$

Similarly,

$$h_{xx} = h_{uu} + h_{vu} + h_{uv} + h_{vv}.$$

Then (ii) is equivalent to

(iii) $$a^2 \cdot (h_{uv} + h_{vu}) = 0.$$

Now we know that if h is a reasonably well-behaved function of u and v, then $h_{uv} = h_{vu}$. In this case, (iii) is equivalent to $h_{uv} = 0$; that is, the v-derivative of h_u is zero, whence h_u depends on u only.

Then, for some α,

$$h_u = \alpha(u) \quad \text{for every } u.$$

Now let β be such that $\beta' = \alpha$. Then

$$\{h - \beta(u)\}_u = h_u - \beta'(u) = \alpha(u) - \alpha(u) = 0 \quad \text{for every } u.$$

Therefore $h - \beta(u)$ depends on v only, say:

$$h - \beta(u) = \gamma(v).$$

Thus if (ii) holds, for some β and γ,

$$h = \beta(u) + \gamma(v) \quad \text{for every } u \text{ and } v;$$

and so if (i) holds, for some β and γ,

(iv) $$\phi(x, t) = \beta(x - a \cdot t) + \gamma(x + a \cdot t),$$

for every x and t.

It is obvious that for any twice-differentiable β and γ this does give a solution of (i). We have found the general solution of (i) under the condition that ϕ is well enough behaved to ensure that

$$\phi_{12}(x, t) = \phi_{21}(x, t)$$

for every x and t. (And worse-behaved solutions, if any, are of no practical interest.)

The reason why this equation is important in physics is that it represents a wave motion. Let us consider, for instance, a vibrating string or a vibrating column of gas. Let y cm be the displacement of a particle of the string (or gas), distant x cm from one end, at time t sec. ("Displacement" means signed distance from equilibrium position.)

Then $y = \beta(x - a \cdot t)$ is the equation of a wave travelling with velocity a cm/sec (in the direction of the x-axis).

To see this, let us imagine a movie screen on which at time t the graph of $\beta(x - a \cdot t)$ against x is shown. At time zero the graph shown has equation

$$y = \beta(x),$$

and as time passes, that is, as t changes, the graph will move.

Let P be any point $\{z, \beta(z)\}$ on the graph at time zero. Let P move parallel to the x-axis with velocity a cm/sec. Then at time t its coordinates are $\{z + a \cdot t, \beta(z)\}$. But the graph showing at time t has equation $y = \beta(x - a \cdot t)$, and these coordinates satisfy this equation. That is, as time passes, P remains on the graph. This is true for every point of the graph, and so the graph moves bodily with velocity a cm/sec. Therefore, we have a wave moving with this velocity. The shape of the wave depends, of course, on β.

Similarly, $y = \gamma(x + a \cdot t)$ represents a wave whose velocity is $-a$ cm/sec.

Let us go one step farther. Suppose that a string is fixed at two points, l cm apart, and is vibrating according to equation (iv). Let us take the origin at one of these points. Because the string is fixed there, $y = 0$ at

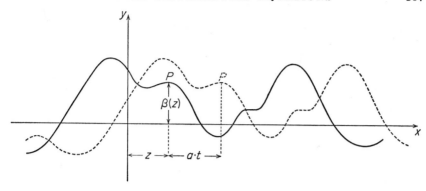

that point for every t. Also, if the other fixed point is $(0, l)$ then $y = 0$ when $x = l$, for every t. That is,

$$\beta(-a \cdot t) + \gamma(a \cdot t) = 0, \quad \text{and} \quad \beta(l - a \cdot t) + \gamma(l + a \cdot t) = 0,$$

for every t. Thus

$$\beta(w) + \gamma(-w) = 0 \quad \text{for every } w,$$

and

$$\beta(w) + \gamma(2l - w) = 0 \quad \text{for every } w.$$

Then $\gamma(-w) = \gamma(2l - w)$ for every w. Thus γ is periodic, and has a period $2l$. This holds also for β. Thus $\gamma(x + a \cdot t) + \beta(x - a \cdot t)$ is, (i) for a fixed t, periodic in x with a period $2l$, and (ii) for a fixed x, periodic in t with a period $2l/a$.

Part II

THE UNDERLYING THEORY

This part, in which we shall clear up various points which we have ignored or only lightly touched on earlier, is intended to be rigorous. One consequence of this is that we shall not use the dependent-variable notation.

In **M** we shall give the proofs which we omitted in **D3** and **B7**.

In **N** we shall investigate further the conditions under which an equation $\phi(x, y) = 0$ defines y as a function of x.

In **O** we shall look more closely than we have done at functions whose values are undefined for some values of the arguments. Some of these functions arise quite naturally.

In **P** we shall prove that certain maxima and minima actually do exist.

M

Proofs of the Fundamental
Theorems

1.

Just as for singulary functions, many properties spring from the idea of a limit. Limits in regard to the various variables separately are nothing new.

$$\lim_{y \to 0} \sin (x \cdot y)/\sin (y \cdot z)$$

is completely analogous to

$$\lim_{y \to 0} \sin 2y/\sin 3y;$$

and the definition of

$$\lim_{y \to b} \psi(x, y, z)$$

is completely analogous to the definition of

$$\lim_{y \to b} \theta(y).$$

111

But what about

$$\lim_{(x,y)\to(a,b)} \phi(x, y),$$

say, where x and y tend to a and b simultaneously? We might be tempted to define it to be

$$\lim_{x\to a} \{\lim_{y\to b} \phi(x, y)\}.$$

There are two things wrong with this. First why should the limit not be

$$\lim_{y\to b} \{\lim_{x\to a} \phi(x, y)\}?$$

We cannot define it to be both because the two are not necessarily equal. For example,

$$\lim_{x\to 0} \{\lim_{y\to 0} (x - y)/(x + y)\} = 1;$$

$$\lim_{y\to 0} \{\lim_{x\to 0} (x - y)/(x + y)\} = -1.$$

The second, and more serious, objection to this definition is that it is of little use. Binary limits defined in this way would not have the properties we should like them to have; namely, properties analogous to the singulary ones. So we start again, considering carefully the definition of limit for a singulary function, and try to find a good analogy to this for binary functions. Once we have solved the problem for binary functions, it will be obvious what the solution will be for n-ary functions in general.

2.

We say that $\psi(x) \to l$ as $x \to 0$, if $\psi(x)$ is as near as we like to l, whenever x is near enough to 0. To make this a precise definition, we need to say exactly what we mean by "as near as we like" and "near enough." This is done in the theory of singulary functions, and the result is

$$\psi(x) \to l \quad \text{as} \quad x \to 0$$

if, given any positive a, there is a positive b such that $\psi(x)$ is between $l - a$ and $l + a$ whenever

$$0 < |x| < b,$$

or words to that effect.

Of course, $\psi(x)$ cannot tend to more than one number as $x \to 0$, as is proved in the theory of singulary functions. If it tends to l we say that l is the *limit* of ψ at a:

$$\lim_{a} \psi = l.$$

If $\psi(x)$ does not tend to any number as $x \to a$, we say that $\lim_{a} \psi$ does not exist. $\lim_{a} \psi$ is sometimes written $\lim_{x\to a} \psi(x)$ or $\lim_{z\to a} \psi(z)$, and so on. It clearly does not matter which letter we use to denote the argument, provided that the letter is not used elsewhere in the formula to denote something else.

Notice that we cannot logically write $\lim_{a} \psi = l$, until we have proved that there is only *one* limit. If there were more than one (say p and q, where $p \neq q$), and if we wrote $\lim_{a} = l$ whenever $\psi(x) \to l$ as $x \to a$, we should have $p = \lim_{a} \psi = q$, and so two unequal numbers would be equal!

3.

So much is review. We now turn to binary functions. We want to make precise the following definition.

$\phi(x, y) \to l$ as $(x, y) \to (0, 0)$ if $\phi(x, y)$ is as near as we like to l whenever (x, y) is near enough to $(0, 0)$. "As near as we like" can mean the same as before, but we must ask ourselves what is meant by "whenever (x, y) is near enough to $(0, 0)$"; that is, under what conditions does a property hold for every (x, y) "near enough" to $(0, 0)$. Geometrical intuition gives us a hint: we can make the phrase mean "whenever (x, y) is in a small enough circle about $(0, 0)$." Thus we finish with the following precise definition. First we define $|h, k|$ to be $(h^2 + k^2)^{1/2}$.

(i)   *Definition.* $\phi(x, y) \to l$ as $(x, y) \to (u, v)$ if, given any positive a, there is a positive b such that $\phi(x, y)$ is between $l - a$ and $l + a$, whenever $0 < |x - u, y - v| < b$. It is clear that there is, given ϕ, at most one such l; if there is one, we call it the limit of ϕ at (u, v) and denote it by $\lim_{(u,v)} \phi$ or

$$\lim_{x \to u, y \to v} \phi(x, y) \text{ etc.}$$

We call the set of all pairs (x, y) for which

$$|x - u, y - v| < b,$$

a *neighborhood* of (u, v), and we call b the *radius* of the neighborhood. Notice the rather subtle distinction between "(u, v) is near enough to (x, y)," and "(u, v) is in some neighborhood of (x, y)." The second allows (u, v) to be (x, y) itself; the first does not. To remember the difference, we recall that one's community neighborhood consists of a number of houses, including one's own, but that one would not say "my house is near itself." Both concepts are useful in the theory to come.

Notice that if

$$\phi(x, y) \to l \quad \text{as} \quad (x, y) \to (0, 0),$$

then for every t

(ii) $\phi(h \cdot \cos t, h \cdot \sin t) \to l$ as $h \to 0$.

The converse is not true: for example, let

$$\phi(x, y) = \begin{cases} 0 & \text{if } y \leqslant 0 \text{ or } y \geqslant x^2 \\ 1 & \text{if } 0 < y < x^2 \end{cases}$$

Then $\phi(h \cdot \cos t, h \cdot \sin t) \to 0$ as $h \to 0$; but in any neighborhood N of $(0, 0)$

we can find points where the value of ϕ is 1 and points where the value is zero. (In the first diagram the value of ϕ is 1 at the shaded points, zero elsewhere.) We can interpret (ii) geometrically; in the second diagram the

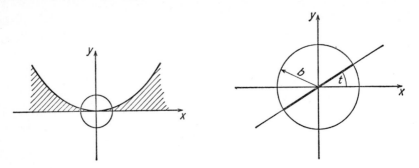

radius of the circle is b and the angle of slope of the line is t. Then the set of all points $(h \cdot \cos t, h \cdot \sin t)$ for $|h| < b$ is the set of points on the thickened segment of the line. We sometimes informally speak of (x, y) "tending to $(0, 0)$ along the line."

Similarly, we sometimes call the limit of $\phi\{\alpha(t), \beta(t)\}$ as $t \to k$ the "limit of $\phi(x, y)$ as (x, y) tends to $\{\alpha(k), \beta(k)\}$ along the curve $x = \alpha(t)$, $y = \beta(t)$."

4.

Illustrations

(i)
$$\phi(x, y) = \begin{cases} 0 & \text{if } x = 0 \\ y & \text{if } x > 0 \\ -y & \text{if } x < 0. \end{cases}$$

Then $\phi(x, y)$ is always between $-|x, y|$ and $|x, y|$, and so if we take 0 for l and, given a, take a itself for b, then the conditions of 3(i) are satisfied. Then $\lim_{(0,0)} \phi = 0$. For comparison, let us investigate $\lim_{y \to 0} \{\lim_{x \to 0} \phi(x, y)\}$. Here $\lim_{x \to 0} \phi(x, y)$ does not exist if $y \neq 0$, because the value of $\phi(x, y)$ jumps from $-y$ to y as the value of x changes from negative to positive. Therefore the repeated limit does not exist.

(ii)
$$\phi(x, y) = \begin{cases} x \cdot y/(x^2 + y^2) & \text{if } x \cdot y \neq 0 \\ 0 & \text{if } x \cdot y = 0 \end{cases}$$

Then, if $h \neq 0$, $\phi(h \cdot \cos t, h \cdot \sin t) = \cos t \cdot \sin t$; and so the limit of $\phi(h \cdot \cos t, h \cdot \sin t)$ as $h \to 0$ is $\cos t \cdot \sin t$. Thus there is *no* l to which $\phi(h \cdot \cos t, h \cdot \sin t)$ tends for every t, and so $\lim_{(0,0)} \phi$ does not exist.

However, the limit along any line such as that in the second diagram in section 3 does exist.

This time
$$\lim_{y \to 0} \{\lim_{x \to 0} \phi(x, y)\} = \lim_{y \to 0} 0 = 0.$$

Note. These illustrations show that the limit at $(0, 0)$ and the repeated limit are "independent" inasmuch as either can exist without the other. However, it is comforting to know that if both exist they must be equal.
Problem. Prove this.

5.

The student should not think⋅we have "cheated" in 4 when we used two or three different formulas to define ϕ. Such definitions are perfectly valid.

What we need to do to define a singulary function ψ is precisely the following: for each and every number x to say whether $\psi(x)$ exists, and if so what its value is. It does not matter how many formulas we need to do this. After all, a definition of the reasonably familiar modulus function is as follows:
$$|x| = \begin{cases} x & \text{if } x \geqslant 0 \\ -x & \text{if } x < 0. \end{cases}$$

Moreover, if the weight of a particle which weighs 1 gm at the earth's surface is $\psi(x)$ gm when it is at a distance x cm from the earth's center, then ψ is given by
$$\psi(x) = \begin{cases} r^2/x^2 & \text{if } x \geqslant r \\ x/r & \text{if } 0 < x < r, \end{cases}$$

or at least it would be if the earth were a uniform sphere of radius r cm. And, finally, if $\phi(t)$ cm is the height of a bouncing ball t seconds after it was dropped, we need an infinite number of formulas to describe ϕ. The formula for $\phi(t)$ changes each time the ball bounces.

The same applies to n-ary functions. The reason why functions defined by single formulas are so prominent in earlier chapters (and indeed in most calculus texts) is that most of the functions which occur in practice are like this. But in a rigorous theory we cannot ignore the awkward minority.

6.

For singulary functions we have a number of theorems on the lines of "the limit of a sum is the sum of the limits." Analogous theorems are true for n-ary functions.

THEOREM. If $\psi(x, y) \to l$, and $\phi(x, y) \to m$ as $(x, y) \to (a, b)$, then
$$\psi(x, y) + \phi(x, y) \to l + m \quad \text{as} \quad (x, y) \to (a, b).$$
Proof. Given any positive k there is a c and a d such that $\psi(x, y)$ is

within $\frac{1}{2}k$ of l whenever (x, y) is within c of (a, b) and $\phi(x, y)$ is within $\frac{1}{2}k$ of m whenever (x, y) is within d of (a, b). Hence, there is a g; namely, the smaller of c and d, such that $\psi(x, y) + \phi(x, y)$ is within k of $l + m$ whenever (x, y) is within g of (a, b). This proof is a straightforward modification of the singulary one. Similar modifications yield the following.

THEOREM. If $\psi(x, y) \to l$, and $\phi(x, y) \to m$ as $(x, y) \to (a, b)$, then
$$\psi(x, y) \cdot \phi(x, y) \to l \cdot m \quad \text{as} \quad (x, y) \to (a, b).$$

THEOREM. If $\phi(x, y) \to m$ as $(x, y) \to (a, b)$, and if $m \neq 0$, then
$$1/\phi(x, y) \to 1/m \quad \text{as} \quad (x, y) \to (a, b).$$

We also have analogues of the simple limit theorems
$$\text{``}x \to a \quad \text{as} \quad x \to a,\text{''} \quad \text{and} \quad \text{``}k \to k \quad \text{as} \quad x \to a\text{''}$$
(which perhaps look less bizarre in the form $\lim_{x \to a} x = a$, and $\lim_{x \to a} k = k$):

THEOREM. If $\phi(x, y) = k$ for every (x, y) near enough to (a, b), then
$$\lim_{(a,b)} \phi = k.$$

THEOREM. If $\phi(x, y) = x$ for every (x, y) near enough to (a, b), then
$$\lim_{(a,b)} \phi = a.$$

THEOREM. If $\phi(x, y) = y$ for every (x, y) near enough to (a, b), then
$$\lim_{(a,b)} \phi = b.$$

Finally we have:

THEOREM. If $\lim_{(a,b)} \phi = l$, $\lim_{c} \alpha = a$, $\lim_{c} \beta = b$, and ϕ is continuous at (a, b), then
$$\lim_{t \to c} \phi\{\alpha(t), \beta(t)\} = l.$$

The same result holds if we replace "ϕ is continuous at (a, b)" by "for every t near enough to c, $\{\alpha(t), \beta(t)\} \neq (a, b)$." (For the corresponding singulary theorems, see H. A. Thurston, *Differentiation and Integration*, Blackie, 1961, p. 41.) The limit which we have proved equal to l is the one which we described informally as the limit of $\phi(x, y)$ as (x, y) tends to (a, b) along the curve $x = \alpha(t)$, $y = \beta(t)$. Thus the theorem can be informally stated: "If $\phi(x, y) \to l$ as $(x, y) \to (a, b)$, then $\phi(x, y) \to l$ as $(x, y) \to (a, b)$ along any path."

7.

We make what is now the obvious definition of continuity: ϕ is *continuous* at (a, b) if $\lim_{(a,b)} \phi = \phi(a, b)$.

8.

It follows straight from the definition in **7** and the limit-theorems in **6** (just as for singular functions) that:

THEOREM. *If ϕ and ψ are continuous at (a, b), then so are $\phi + \psi$ and $\phi \cdot \psi$. If, also, $\psi(a, b) \neq 0$, then ϕ/ψ, too, is continuous there.*

Note. $\phi + \psi$ is, of course, the function ξ for which

$$\xi(x, y) = \phi(x, y) + \psi(x, y),$$

and similarly for $\phi \cdot \psi$ and ϕ/ψ.

9.

Let us consider continuity for a binary function graphically. Let A be the point (a, b) in the xy-plane, and A^* the point above A on the graph of ϕ; that is, A^* is $(a, b, \phi\{a, b\})$.

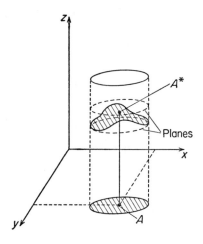

Let P be any point in the xy-plane, and P^* the point above it on the graph of ϕ. Thus if P is $(x, y, 0)$, then P^* is $(x, y, \phi\{x, y\})$.

Then the condition that ϕ shall be continuous at (a, b) is, that given any positive k, there should be some neighborhood of (a, b)—for example, the shaded circle—such that the height of P^* is within k of the height of A^* whenever P is in the neighborhood. That is, given any two horizontal planes sandwiching A^* between them, there should be a cylinder as in the diagram, such that the part of the graph of ϕ inside the cylinder is wholly sandwiched between the planes.

10.

Now consider the function ϕ defined by

$$\phi(x, y) = \begin{cases} 1 & \text{if } x \cdot y \geq 0. \\ 0 & \text{if } x \cdot y < 0. \end{cases}$$

Its graph is shown in diagram (i); it consists of parts of two planes, of heights 0 and 1. The height is 0 in the fourth and second quadrants; 1 in the first and third and along the coordinate axes.

Is ϕ continuous at $(0, 0)$? Because $\phi(0, 0) = 1$, the question is: "Can we, given any positive k, find a neighborhood N of $(0, 0)$, such that $\phi(x, y)$

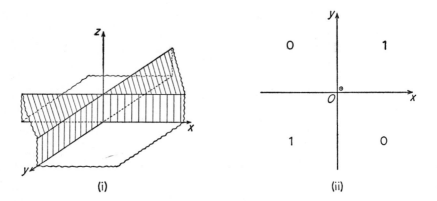

(i)   (ii)

is within k of 1 whenever (x, y) is in N?" The neighborhood will be a circle about $(0, 0)$—like the shaded circle about A. Let us take a particular case: $k = \frac{1}{2}$. Can we find a circle about $(0, 0)$, such that $\frac{1}{2} < \phi(x, y) < 1\frac{1}{2}$ for every (x, y) in the circle? The answer is obviously no. *Whatever* circle about $(0, 0)$ we choose, $\phi(x, y)$ will be zero for some (x, y) in the circle. Thus ϕ is not continuous at $(0, 0)$.

Is ϕ continuous at $(\frac{1}{100}, \frac{1}{100})$? Yes: given *any* positive k, the circle of radius $\frac{1}{200}$ about this point will do for N, because for every (x, y) in that circle, $\phi(x, y) = 1$ and so $\phi(x, y) = \phi(\frac{1}{100}, \frac{1}{100})$, which is obviously within k of $\phi(\frac{1}{100}, \frac{1}{100})$.

It should be clear now just where ϕ is continuous and where it is not. It is discontinuous on the coordinate axes (that is, the edges of the shaded "plateau" in diagram i); and continuous everywhere else.

Arguments of this sort can be used in general. If the graph of ϕ can be visualized, ϕ will be discontinuous at "vertical cliffs," "pot-holes," and similar places, and continuous elsewhere.

11.

Now let us consider α where

$$\alpha(x, y) = \begin{cases} x \cdot y/(x^2 + y^2) & \text{whenever} \quad (x, y) \neq (0, 0) \\ 0 & \text{when} \quad (x, y) = (0, 0). \end{cases}$$

Where is this continuous? The student who is familiar with three-dimensional graphs can visualize the graph of α and so answer the question. Even without this, however, the answer is quite easy.

$$x \to a \quad \text{as} \quad (x, y) \to (a, b)$$

and

$$y \to b \quad \text{as} \quad (x, y) \to (a, b)$$

and so, by the theorems about sums, products, etc., of limits,

$$(x^2 + y^2) \to (a^2 + b^2) \quad \text{as} \quad (x, y) \to (a, b)$$

and

$$x \cdot y \to a \cdot b \quad \text{as} \quad (x, y) \to (a, b).$$

Then

$$x \cdot y/(x^2 + y^2) \to a \cdot b/(a^2 + b^2) \quad \text{as} \quad (x, y) \to (a, b)$$

provided $(a^2 + b^2) \neq 0$. This proviso is satisfied unless we happen to have $(a, b) = (0, 0)$. Thus if $(a, b) \neq (0, 0)$; then

$$\alpha(x, y) \to \alpha(a, b) \quad \text{as} \quad (x, y) \to (a, b)$$

and so α is continuous at (a, b). $\lim_{(0,0)} \alpha$ does not exist, as we saw in 4(ii); therefore α is not continuous at $(0, 0)$.

12.

We know that a continuous function of a continuous singulary function is continuous. In general, a continuous m-ary function of m continuous n-ary functions is continuous. If the functions are not continuous everywhere, the theorem applies where they are continuous; just as cosec log is continuous at 2, because log is continuous at 2 and cosec is continuous at log 2.

We shall state the theorem for a function of two singulary functions as an example.

THEOREM. If ξ and η are continuous at a and if ϕ is continuous at $\{\xi(a), \eta(a)\}$, and if $\psi(x) = \phi\{\xi(x), \eta(x)\}$, for every x near enough to a, then ψ is continuous at a. This follows at once from the last theorem of **6**.

13.

We can obtain many properties of binary functions in which "one variable at a time" is involved directly from the corresponding properties of singulary functions. In this section we list a few that we shall find useful later. We reduce a binary ϕ to singular functions as follows: For each y define functions $\xi^{(y)}$ and $\eta^{(y)}$ by

$$\xi^{(y)}(x) = \phi(x, y), \quad \eta^{(y)}(x) = \phi(y, x)$$

(for every x for which the respective right-hand sides exist).

DEFINITIONS.

ϕ is 1-continuous at (x, y) if $\xi^{(y)}$ is continuous at x.

ϕ is 1-differentiable at (x, y) if $\xi^{(y)}$ is differentiable at x.

ϕ is 2-continuous at (x, y) if $\eta^{(x)}$ is continuous at y.

ϕ is 2-differentiable at (x, y) if $\eta^{(x)}$ is differentiable at y. We can define 1-increasing, 2-monotonic, etc., similarly.

(i) THEOREM. If, given x, y, and h, ϕ is 1-differentiable at (u, y) whenever u is between x and $x + h$, and 1-continuous at (x, y) and $(x + h, y)$, then there is a t between 0 and 1 such that

$$\phi(x + h, y) = \phi(x, y) + h \cdot \phi_1(x + t \cdot h, y).$$

Proof. Apply the mean-value theorem ("law of the mean") to $\xi^{(y)}$.

Note. We really require only semi-1-continuity (just as we require only semi-continuity for the singular mean-value theorem). For example, if h is positive, it is enough to have

$$\lim_{u \to x+} \phi(u, y) = \phi(x, y);$$

we do not need $\lim_{u \to x} \phi(u, y) = \phi(x, y)$. Indeed, $\phi(u, y)$ need not be defined unless u is x or $x + h$ or between these. We have a similar result if ϕ is 2-differentiable.

14.

We can put the condition for differentiability which we had in **16** in a slightly more convenient form as follows. Define α by

$$\alpha(h, k) = \begin{cases} 0 & \text{if} \quad (h, k) = (0, 0) \\ (\Delta z - \Delta^* z)/|h, k| & \text{whenever this is defined.} \end{cases}$$

Then **11**(ii) becomes: $\alpha(h, k) \to 0$ as $(h, k) \to (0, 0)$; that is, α is continuous at $(0, 0)$. Hence, replacing Δz and $\Delta^* z$ by the formulas they abbreviate, ϕ is differentiable at (a, b) if, and only if, there is a function α, continuous at $(0, 0)$, such that $\alpha(0, 0) = 0$, and

$$\phi(a + h, b + k) - \phi(a, b) - h \cdot \phi_1(a, b) - k \cdot \phi_2(a, b) = |h, k| \cdot \alpha(h, k),$$

for every (h, k) in some neighborhood of $(0, 0)$.

15.

The chain-rule gives a formula for the derivative of a function of m n-ary functions. The case $m = n = 1$ is misleadingly simple; we shall prove the case $m = 2$, $n = 1$ and deduce the case $m = n = 2$. This will illustrate the general proof.

THEOREM. *If* $\xi(a) = b$ *and* $\eta(a) = c$, $\xi'(a)$ *and* $\eta'(a)$ *exist, and* ϕ *is differentiable at* (b, c), *and if* $\psi(x) = \phi\{\xi(x), \eta(x)\}$ *for every* x *in some neighborhood of* a, *then* $\psi'(a)$ *exists and equals*

(i)
$$\phi_1(b, c)\cdot\xi'(a) + \phi_2(b, c)\cdot\eta'(a)$$

Proof. Denote $\xi(a + h) - b$ by u and $\eta(a + h) - c$ by v. Then,

(ii) $\psi(a + h) - \psi(a) = \phi(b + u, c + v) - \phi(b, c)$
$$= u\cdot\phi_1(b, c) + v\cdot\phi_2(b, c) + |u, v|\cdot\alpha(u, v)$$

where $\alpha(0, 0) = 0$ and α is continuous at $(0, 0)$. We shall consider what happens when we divide by h and let $h \to 0$.

$$\left|\frac{u\cdot\alpha(u, v)}{h}\right| = \left|\frac{\xi(a + h) - \xi(a)}{h}\right|\cdot|\alpha\{\xi(a + h) - \xi(a), \eta(a + h) - \eta(a)\}|.$$

The second factor tends to zero and the first to $\xi'(a)$, and so

$$|u\cdot\alpha(u, v)/h| \to 0 \quad \text{as} \quad h \to 0.$$

Similarly, so does $|v\cdot\alpha(u, v)/h|$ and, hence, so does their sum.

$$|u, v| \leqslant |u| + |v|,$$

and so

$$|u, v|\cdot\alpha(u, v)/h \to 0 \quad \text{as} \quad h \to 0.$$

$$u\cdot\phi_1(b, c)/h = \frac{\xi(a + h) - \xi(a)}{h}\cdot\phi_1(b, c) \to \phi_1(b, c)\cdot\xi'(a) \quad \text{as} \quad h \to 0.$$

Similarly,

$$v\cdot\phi_2(b, c)/h \to \phi_2(b, c)\cdot\eta'(a).$$

Therefore $\lim_{h\to 0} \{\psi(a + h) - \psi(a)\}/h$ exists and equals (i).

16.

Now let us suppose that the ξ and η in **15** are binary. We then apply the theorem to the functions α and β defined by $\alpha(x) = \xi(x, b)$, and $\beta(x) = \eta(x, b)$, or to the functions defined by $\alpha(x) = \xi(a, x)$, and $\beta(x) = \eta(a, x)$. This gives the following theorem.

THEOREM. *If* $i = 1$ *or* 2, *if* $\xi_i(a, b)$ *and* $\eta_i(a, b)$ *exist, if* $\xi(a, b) = c$ *and*

$\eta(a, b) = d$, if ϕ is differentiable at (c, d), and if $\psi(x, y) = \phi\{\xi(x, y), \eta(x, y)\}$ for every (x, y) in some neighborhood of (a, b), then

$$\psi_i(a, b) = \phi_1(c, d)\cdot\xi_i(a, b) + \phi_2(c, d)\cdot\eta_i(a, b).$$

The generalization to n m-ary functions is now clear.

17.

We now supply the missing proof promised in **B7**.

THEOREM. If ϕ_1 and ϕ_2 are differentiable at (a, b), then

$$\phi_{12}(a, b) = \phi_{21}(a, b)$$

Proof. Let $\omega(h)$ be

$$\phi(a + h, b + h) - \phi(a + h, b) - \phi(a, b + h) + \phi(a, b).$$

For each h, let $\psi(x)$ be $\phi(x, b + h) - \phi(x, b)$. Because ϕ_1 and ϕ_2 are differentiable at (a, b), there must be a neighborhood N of (a, b) throughout which they (and a fortiori ϕ also), are defined. Then there is a neighborhood of a throughout which ψ' is defined and so, by the mean-value theorem, if $a + h$ is in this neighborhood there is a t between 0 and h inclusive, such that

$$\psi(a + h) - \psi(a) = h\cdot\psi'(a + t).$$

Define σ by letting $\sigma(h)$ be t/h if $\cdot h \neq 0$, and $\sigma(0) = 0$.* Then $\sigma(h)$ is bounded (it lies between 0 and 1), and $h\cdot\sigma(h)$ is a function of h which is continuous at $h = 0$. Then,

$$
\begin{aligned}
\omega(h) &= \psi(a + h) - \psi(a) \\
&= h\cdot\psi'(a + t) \\
&= h\cdot\{\phi_1(a + t, b + h) - \phi_1(a + t, b)\} \\
&= h\cdot\{\phi_1(a + t, b + h) - \phi_1(a, b)\} - h\cdot\{\phi_1(a + t, b) - \phi_1(a, b)\} \\
&= h\cdot\{t\cdot\phi_{11}(a, b) + h\cdot\phi_{12}(a, b) + |t, h|\cdot\alpha(t, h)\} \\
&\quad - h\cdot\{t\cdot\phi_{11}(a, b) + |t|\cdot\alpha(t, 0)\} \text{ for some } \alpha \text{ continuous at } (0, 0) \\
&\quad\quad \text{for which } \alpha(0, 0) = 0 \\
&= h^2\cdot\phi_{12}(a, b) + h\cdot|t, h|\cdot\alpha(t, h) - h\cdot|t|\cdot\alpha(t, 0).
\end{aligned}
$$

Then

$$\omega(h)/h^2 = \phi_{12}(a, b) + h^{-1}\cdot|h|\cdot|\sigma(h), 1|\cdot\alpha\{h\cdot\sigma(h), h\}$$
$$- h^{-1}\cdot|h\cdot\sigma(h)|\cdot\alpha\{h\cdot\sigma(h), 0\}.$$

Because α is continuous at $(0, 0)$, both factors involving α tend to zero as

---

* The mathematical logician will notice that this proof uses the selection axiom (multiplicative axiom) because we cannot *specify* the value of t for each h; we know only that at least one exists for each h.

$h \to 0$. Because $\sigma(h)$ is bounded, both terms containing these factors tend to zero. Therefore

$$\omega(h)/h^2 \to \phi_{12}(a, b) \quad \text{as} \quad h \to 0.$$

By symmetry, it also tends to $\phi_{21}(a, b)$.

18.

We have given the proofs of the chain-rule and the "$\phi_{12} = \phi_{21}$" theorem for differentiable ϕ. In the first part of the book, for practical reasons, we quoted and used these results before considering differentiability. We explained in **17** that ϕ is differentiable if its first-order derivatives are continuous. We now prove this; in fact, we prove a stronger result. This, then, completes the proof of these theorems under the conditions quoted in the first part.

THEOREM. If ϕ_1 is continuous at (x, y) and $\phi_2(x, y)$ exists, then ϕ is differentiable at (x, y).

Proof. ϕ_1 must be defined near (x, y), and so, for every (h, k) near enough to $(0, 0)$, by the mean-value theorem,

$$\phi(x + h, y + k) - \phi(x, y + k) = h \cdot \phi_1(x + t \cdot h, y + k)$$

where $0 < t < 1$. Also,

$$\phi(x, y + k) - \phi(x, y) = k \cdot \phi_2(x, y) + k \cdot \rho(k)$$

where $\rho(k) \to 0$ as $k \to 0$. Therefore

$$\left| \frac{\phi(x + h, y + k) - \phi(x, y) - h \cdot \phi_1(x, y) - k \cdot \phi_2(x, y)}{|h, k|} \right|$$

$$= \left| \frac{h \cdot \{\phi_1(x + t \cdot h, y + k) - \phi_1(x, y)\} + k \cdot \rho(k)}{|h, k|} \right|$$

$$\leqslant |\phi_1(x + t \cdot h, y + k) - \phi_1(x, y)| + |\rho(k)| \to 0 \quad \text{as} \quad (h, k) \to (0, 0)$$

as we see by putting $t = \sigma(h, k)$, bearing in mind the footnote to **17**, and noting that $h \cdot \sigma(h, k) \to 0$ as $h \to 0$.

A similar proof gives the general n-ary theorem: if one first-order derivative is continuous at $(x_1, \ldots, x_n)$ and the others are defined there, then the function is differentiable there.

It is worth noting that the converse of this theorem is not true. If, for instance,

$$\phi(x, y) = (x + y) \cdot \alpha(x + y),$$

where α is a function which is everywhere continuous and nowhere differentiable, then ϕ is differentiable at $(0, 0)$, but neither ϕ_1 nor ϕ_2 is continuous there. It is proved in the theory of singulary functions that such a function as α exists.

19.

We now prove the result stated in **K5**.

THEOREM. If ϕ_{11}, ϕ_{12}, ϕ_{21} and ϕ_{22} are continuous in a neighborhood of (a, b), if $\phi_1(a, b) = \phi_2(a, b) = 0$, if $\phi_{11}(a, b) < 0$, and if

$$\phi_{11}(a, b) \cdot \phi_{22}(a, b) - \phi_{12}(a, b)^2 > 0,$$

then ϕ has a local maximum at (a, b).

Proof. There is a positive d such that, whenever $|h, k| < d$ and (x, y) is within d of (a, b), then

$$\phi_{11}(x, y) < 0, \quad \phi_{11}(x, y) \cdot \phi_{22}(x, y) - \phi_{12}(x, y)^2 > 0,$$

and Taylor's formula for $n = 2$ holds:

$$\phi(a + h, b + k) - \phi(a, b) = \tfrac{1}{2}(h^2 \cdot u + 2h \cdot k \cdot v + k^2 \cdot w),$$

where u, v, and w are the values of ϕ_{11}, ϕ_{12}, and ϕ_{22}, respectively, at some point within $|h, k|$ of (a, b). The right-hand side equals

$$\tfrac{1}{2}u \cdot \{(h + v \cdot k/u)^2 + (u \cdot w - v^2) \cdot k^2/u\},$$

which is negative.

N

Implicit Functions

1.

We have seen in **A7** and **D20**, by using geometrical intuition, that the equation $\phi(x, y) = 0$ is locally solvable for y wherever its graph has a unique non-vertical tangent. Our aim here is to state the corresponding result without using diagrams, and to prove it. From **D20** it is to be expected that the curve has a non-vertical tangent at (a, b) provided that $\phi_1(a, b)$ exists and $\phi_2(a, b) \neq 0$. (Incidentally, the converse of this is not true. If $\phi(x, y)$ is $y - x^2$ whenever this is rational, 1 whenever it is not, the graph of $\phi(x, y) = 0$ has a non-vertical tangent at each of its points.) We shall also need a condition to take the place of the condition that the graph of $\phi(x, y) = 0$ is a curve and not a scattered set of points: that is, ϕ has to be reasonably well-behaved. It turns out that we shall want ϕ_1 and ϕ_2 to be continuous at and near (a, b).

We shall prove first a more general (but quite easy) result, not involving derivatives, from which the above will follow.

2.

THEOREM. If $\phi(a, b) = 0$, if N is a neighborhood of (a, b), if $\phi(x, y)$ is defined for every (x, y) in N, if ϕ is 1-continuous and 2-continuous in N, and if ϕ is strictly 2-increasing in N;* then there is a function η and a neighborhood M of (a, b) such that, for every (x, y) in M,

$$\phi(x, y) = 0 \quad \text{if and only if} \quad y = \eta(x),$$

and η is continuous at a.

Note. It may help in following the proof if we consider what happens diagrammatically. Let the circle in the diagram represent N: its center, O, has coordinates (a, b). Draw the vertical diameter, and on it take any two points P, Q, equidistant from O. Because the value of ϕ at O is zero, and because $\phi(x, y)$ increases with increasing y, we can say that $\phi(x, y)$ will be positive at P and negative at Q. Draw a horizontal line through P. By continuity, there will be a segment of this line about P on which the values of ϕ are all positive. Similarly, there will be a horizontal segment about Q on which the values of ϕ are negative. Hence, we can construct

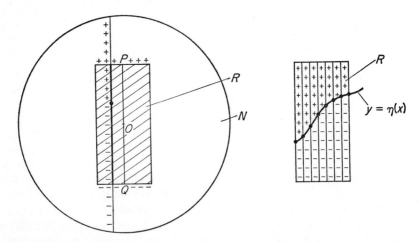

the shaded rectangle R: on its top edge ϕ has positive values; on its bottom edge, negative. Now let us consider any vertical line in the rectangle. At the bottom, $\phi(x, y)$ is negative, and it increases continuously up the line until at the top it is positive. Hence, there is one (and only one) point on

---

* This means, of course, that if (u, v) and (u, w) are in N and $v > w$, then $\phi(u, v) > \phi(u, w)$.

the line where it is zero. The ordinate of this point depends on the abscissa of the line, so we can call it $\eta(x)$. This is the η we want, because we have so defined it that $\phi\{x, \eta(x)\} = 0$, and (given x) $\eta(x)$ is the only ordinate (at least, the only one in the circle) with this property. We can take for M any neighborhood of O contained in R. Now all we have to do is to formalize this argument.

Proof. Let the radius of N be r and let c be between 0 and r. Then $(a, b - c)$ and $(a, b + c)$ are in N. Then, because $\phi(a, b) = 0$ and $\phi(a, y)$ increases strictly with y,

$$\phi(a, b - c) < 0 < \phi(a, b + c).$$

Because ϕ is 1-continuous in N, there is a d_1 such that $(x, b - c)$ is in N and $\phi(x, b - c) < 0$, whenever x is within d_1 of a; and similarly for $\phi(x, b + c) > 0$ and d_2. Let d be the smaller of d_1 and d_2. Then

$$\phi(x, b - c) < 0 < \phi(x, b + c),$$

whenever x is within d of a. Moreover, for each such x, (x, y) is in N whenever $b - c \leqslant y \leqslant b + c$. Also, ϕ is 2-continuous in N. Therefore there is, for each such x, a number $\eta(x)$ between $b - c$ and $b + c$ for which

(i) $$\phi\{x, \eta(x)\} = 0.$$

Now let M be the neighborhood of O whose radius is d, and let (x, y) be in M. Then $\eta(x)$ is defined. Then, firstly, if $y = \eta(x)$, it follows from (i) that $\phi(x, y) = 0$, because x is within d of a. And, secondly, if $\phi(x, y) = 0$, we cannot have $y > \eta(x)$, because then

$$\phi(x, y) > \phi\{x, \eta(x)\} = 0;$$

and similarly $y \nless \eta(x)$; and so $y = \eta(x)$.

Finally, let us prove that η is continuous at a. Let h be any positive number: we must prove that there is a g such that $\eta(x)$ is within h of b, whenever x is within g of a.

In the proof above of (i), c was any positive number less than r. Let us repeat the proof, but now taking c to be any positive number less than h and r. We find, as before, that whenever x is within d of a, $\eta(x)$ is between $b - c$ and $b + c$; and, therefore, between $b - h$ and $b + h$. That is, $\eta(x)$ is within h of b, whenever x is within d of a. This is what we required, taking d for our g.

3.

COROLLARY. If we replace "increasing" by "decreasing" in theorem 2, the conclusion still holds.

4.

THEOREM. If $\phi(a, b) = 0$, and if ϕ_1 and ϕ_2 are continuous near and at (a, b), and if $\phi_2(a, b) \neq 0$, then there is a function η such that, for every (x, y) in some neighborhood of (a, b)

(i)　　　　　　$\phi(x, y) = 0$　if and only if　$y = \eta(x)$,

and　　　　　　$\eta'(a) = -\phi_1(a, b)/\phi_2(a, b)$.

Note. The important point about the last phrase is that $\eta'(a)$ *exists*. We know already what it must be equal to *if* it exists, by differentiating the equation

$$\phi\{x, \eta(x)\} = 0 \quad \text{re} \quad x.$$

Theorem **2** was an implicit-function theorem for continuous functions. In **4** we have brought up the question of derivatives.

Proof. Because $\phi_2(a, b) \neq 0$ and ϕ_2 is continuous at (a, b), there is a neighborhood of (a, b) in which the values of ϕ_2 are all of the same sign. Then $\phi(x, y)$ is either a strictly increasing or a strictly decreasing function of y in that neighborhood. Therefore, by corollary **3**, η exists satisfying (i).

With c and d as in the first part of the proof of theorem **2**, let h be any positive number less than c and d, and let k denote $\eta(a + h) - \eta(a)$. By Taylor's theorem, there is a t between 0 and 1 for which

$$\phi(a + h, b + k) - \phi(a, b) = h \cdot \phi_1(a + t \cdot h, b + t \cdot k) + k \cdot \phi_2(a + t \cdot h, b + t \cdot k).$$

Now

$$\phi(a + h, b + k) = \phi\{a + h, \eta(a + h)\} = 0.$$

Therefore

$$h \cdot \phi_1(a + t \cdot h, b + t \cdot k) + \{\eta(a + h) - \eta(a)\} \cdot \phi_2(a + t \cdot h, b + t \cdot k) = 0.$$

ϕ_2 is continuous at (a, b), and $\phi_2(a, b) \neq 0$, and so $\phi_2(a + t \cdot h, b + t \cdot k)$ is non-zero for every (h, k) near enough to $(0, 0)$. Also, $k \to 0$ as $h \to 0$ because η is continuous. Therefore for every small enough non-zero h,

$$\frac{\eta(a + h) - \eta(a)}{h} = \frac{-\phi_1(a + t \cdot h, b + t \cdot k)}{\phi_2(a + t \cdot h, b + t \cdot k)}.$$

Then by the footnote to **M17** and the "limit of the quotient" theorem, this tends to the limit $-\phi_1(a, b)/\phi_2(a, b)$ as $h \to 0$. That is, $\eta'(a)$ exists and equals this.

5.

The corresponding results for n-ary functions, in general, are proved similarly. As an example, let us quote a ternary form of theorem **4**:

If $\phi(a, b, c) = 0$, if $\phi_3(a, b, c) \neq 0$, and if ϕ_1, ϕ_2, and ϕ_3 are continuous near and at (a, b, c), then there is a function ζ such that, for every (x, y, z) in some neighborhood of (a, b, c),

$$\phi(x, y, z) = 0 \quad \text{if and only if} \quad z = \zeta(x, y).$$

Moreover, $\zeta_1(a, b)$ and $\zeta_2(a, b)$ exist.

6.

Obviously there is no need for us to single out the *last* argument of ϕ for special treatment. For instance if, in theorem 4, it had been $\phi_1(a, b)$ that had been non-zero, the conclusion would have been: There is a function ξ such that, for every (x, y) in some neighborhood of (a, b), $\phi(x, y) = 0$ if, and only if, $x = \xi(y)$. Moreover, $\xi'(b)$ exists.

7.

As a corollary to theorem 4 we can conclude that η' is continuous at a.

To see this, we simply note that if (u, v) is near enough to (a, b), there is [by theorem 4 applied to (u, v)] a θ such that $\phi(x, y) = 0$ if, and only if, $y = \theta(x)$, at least whenever (x, y) is in some neighborhood of (u, v). And

$$\theta'(u) = -\phi_1(u, v)/\phi_2(u, v).$$

But by theorem 4 applied to (a, b) this happens if, and only if, $y = \eta(x)$. Therefore $\eta(x) = \theta(x)$ for every x in some neighborhood of u, and so $\eta'(u) = \theta'(u)$.

We have now proved that

$$\eta'(u) = -\phi_1(u, v)/\phi_2(u, v),$$

for every u in some neighborhood of a [where $v = \eta(u)$]. ϕ_1 and ϕ_2 are continuous at (a, b), and η at a; also $\eta(a) = b$. Therefore η' is a quotient of functions continuous at a, and so is itself continuous at a.

8.

So much for *one* implicit equation between variables, defining *one* of them as a function of the others. Suppose now that we have *two*; for example

(i) $\qquad\qquad \alpha(u, v, x) = 0 \quad \text{and} \quad \beta(u, v, x) = 0.$

Under what conditions can we prove that they define u and v as functions of x, and what are the derivatives of u and v re x?

As a hint, let us find what the derivatives will be *if* they exist. If $u = \theta(x)$ and $v = \eta(x)$, then from

(ii) $\qquad\quad \alpha\{\theta(x), \eta(x), x\} = 0 \quad \text{and} \quad \beta\{\theta(x), \eta(x), x\} = 0,$

we get

$$\alpha_1\{\theta(x),\, \eta(x),\, x\} \cdot \theta'(x) + \alpha_2\{\theta(x),\, \eta(x),\, x\} \cdot \eta'(x) + \alpha_3\{\theta(x),\, \eta(x),\, x\} = 0$$
$$\beta_1\{\theta(x),\, \eta(x),\, x\} \cdot \theta'(x) + \beta_2\{\theta(x),\, \eta(x),\, x\} \cdot \eta'(x) + \beta_3\{\theta(x),\, \eta(x),\, x\} = 0.$$

These are two linear equations and are easily solved for $\theta'(x)$ and $\eta'(x)$, the required derivatives. There is no need to write out the solution, but let us note that the condition that unique solutions exist is

(iii)
$$\begin{vmatrix} \alpha_1\{\theta(x),\, \eta(x),\, x\} & \alpha_2\{\theta(x),\, \eta(x),\, x\} \\ \beta_1\{\theta(x),\, \eta(x),\, x\} & \beta_2\{\theta(x),\, \eta(x),\, x\} \end{vmatrix} \neq 0.$$

Let us look for a local solution of (i); that is, let us seek functions θ and η, such that $\alpha(a, b, c) = \beta(a, b, c) = 0$ and, for every (u, v, x) in some neighborhood of (a, b, c), (i) holds if, and only if, $u = \theta(x)$ and $v = \eta(x)$. If $x = a$, formula (iii) becomes

(iv)
$$\begin{vmatrix} \alpha_1(a, b, c) & \alpha_2(a, b, c) \\ \beta_1(a, b, c) & \beta_2(a, b, c) \end{vmatrix} \neq 0.$$

We might well expect that (iv) is a condition (analogous to the condition $\phi_2(a, b) \neq 0$ in 4), under which we shall be able to prove the result which we want. This turns out to be true.

Note. In the dependent-variable notation, let f denote $\alpha(u, v, x)$ and g denote $\beta(u, v, x)$. Then the determinant in (iii) becomes

$$\begin{vmatrix} f_u & f_v \\ g_u & g_v \end{vmatrix}.$$

It is known as the *Jacobian* of f and g re u and v, and is sometimes denoted by $\partial(f, g)/\partial(u, v)$.

Having discovered the appropriate conditions, we prove our result by applying implicit function theorems twice: once to u and once to v.

THEOREM. If $\alpha(a, b, c) = \beta(a, b, c) = 0$, if α_1, α_2, β_1, and β_2 are continuous at and near (a, b, c), and if (iv) holds, then there are functions θ and η and a neighborhood M of (a, b, c) such that, for every (u, v, x) in M,

$$\alpha(u, v, x) = \beta(u, v, x)$$

if, and only if,

$$u = \theta(x) \quad \text{and} \quad v = \eta(x).$$

Moreover θ and η are differentiable at c.

Proof. $\alpha_2(a, b, c)$ and $\beta_2(a, b, c)$ are not both zero by (iv). Let us suppose that $\alpha_2(a, b, c) \neq 0$. (The proof is similar in the other case.)

Then, by 5 and 6, there is a ϕ and a neighborhood L of (a, b, c) such that, for every (u, v, x) in L, $\alpha(u, v, x) = 0$ if, and only if, $v = \phi(u, x)$.

If $v = \phi(u, x)$, then $\beta(u, v, x) = 0$ if, and only if, $\gamma(u, x) = 0$, where $\gamma(u, x)$ is $\beta\{u, \phi(u, x), x\}$.

$$\gamma_1(a, c) = \beta_1(a, b, c) + \beta_2(a, b, c) \cdot \phi_1(a, c).$$

Also,

$$\phi_1(a, c) = -\alpha_1(a, b, c)/\alpha_2(a, b, c).$$

Therefore $\gamma_1(a, c) \neq 0$, by (iv).

Then, by theorem 4, there is a θ and a neighborhood N of (a, c) such that, for every (u, x) in N, $\gamma(u, x) = 0$ if, and only if, $u = \theta(x)$.

By 7, θ is differentiable at c. Let $\eta(x)$ be $\phi\{\theta(x), x\}$. By 7, ϕ_1 and ϕ_2 are continuous at (a, c), that is, at $\{\theta(c), c\}$; and so η is differentiable at c, by the chain-rule.

Finally, let M be a neighborhood of (a, b, c) whose radius is smaller than the radii of N and L. Then, for (u, v, x) in M, $u = \theta(x)$ and $v = \eta(x)$ if, and only if,

$$\beta\{u, \phi(u, x), x\} = 0 \quad \text{and} \quad v = \phi(u, x);$$

that is, if, and only if, $\alpha(u, v, x) = 0$ and $\beta(u, v, x) = 0$.

9.

If we have two relations between any number (greater than two) of variables, we get a similar theorem. To state and prove it, all we need do is re-write 8, replacing (u, v, x) by (u, v, x, y), or (u, v, x, y, z), etc., according to how many variables there are (and of course replacing (a, b, c) by appropriate n-ples of numbers).

If we have n relations between more than n variables, we get a similar theorem. The crucial condition will be expressible by means of an $n \times n$ determinant analogous to that in (iv).

10.

We have now made a good start in an advanced branch of the calculus, the theory of Jacobians. We shall not pursue it much further, but we shall just mention two results to give an idea of the way in which it can be applied.

11.

Suppose that we have a pair of equations $x = \xi(u, v)$, $y = \eta(u, v)$. If ξ and η are sufficiently well-behaved, we have the situation of theorem **9** when $n = 4$. If these equations represent, say, a change of system of coordinates, we shall certainly want them to be solvable for u and v, at any rate locally. The condition for this, is that the Jacobian be non-zero.

(Note that the familiar equations

$$x = r \cdot \cos t, \qquad y = r \cdot \sin t$$

are only *locally* solvable [and not even that, if $(x, y) = (0, 0)$.] For example, $(r, t) = (1, 0)$ and $(r, t) = (1, 2\pi)$ both satisfy the equations if

$(x, y) = (1, 0)$. But there is a *neighborhood* of $(1, 0, 1, 0)$ in which there is a unique solution.

Now suppose that we have two planes, in each of which a system of cartesian coordinates is set up. Let us define a "transformation" of the first plane onto the second as follows: the point whose coordinates are (a, b) in the first plane transforms into the point whose coordinates are $\{\xi(a, b), \eta(a, b)\}$ in the second. Given any point (c, d) in the second plane, there may be many, few, or no points in the first which transform into it, according to the number of solutions of the equations

$$\xi(x, y) = c, \quad \eta(x, y) = d.$$

The most interesting case is where there is exactly one solution, because then the transformation is reversible. We define the reverse transformation as follows—given a point in the second plane we let it reverse-transform into the point which transformed into it in the original transformation.

As usual, we are satisfied with *local* reversibility, and the condition for this is that the Jacobian be non-zero. Thus Jacobians are important in the theory of transformations.

12.

Now let us turn to the opposite case. One situation where we *cannot* solve $u = \alpha(x, y)$ and $v = \beta(x, y)$ for x and y, is when α is a function of β (or β a function of α). For example, trying to solve

$$u = x + y, \quad v = \sin(x + y)$$

for x and y is a hopeless task. Let us suppose, then, that α *is* a function of β, say,

$$\alpha(x, y) = \gamma\{\beta(x, y)\}.$$

Now what about the Jacobian? We easily see that

$$\alpha_1(x, y) = \gamma'\{\beta(x, y)\} \cdot \beta_1(x, y),$$

and similarly for α_2, and so the Jacobian is zero.

We naturally ask what other situations make the Jacobian zero, and the answer is that this is the only one if α and β are reasonably well-behaved:

THEOREM. If

$$\begin{vmatrix} \alpha_1(x, y) & \alpha_2(x, y) \\ \beta_1(x, y) & \beta_2(x, y) \end{vmatrix} = 0 \text{ for every } (x, y)$$

in some neighborhood of (a, b); if $\alpha_1, \alpha_2, \beta_1$ and β_2 are continuous there, and if $\alpha_1(a, b) \neq 0$; then there is a ϕ such that

$$\beta(x, y) = \phi\{\alpha(x, y)\}$$

for every (x, y) in some neighborhood of (a, b).

Proof. By the implicit-function theorem there is a θ such that, for every (x, y) in the relevant neighborhood,

$$u - \alpha(x, y) = 0$$

if, and only if, $x = \theta(u, y)$. Moreover,

$$\theta_2\{\alpha(x, y), y\} = -\alpha_2(x, y)/\alpha_1(x, y).$$

Then,

(i) $$\theta_2(u, y) = -\alpha_2\{\theta(u, y), y\}/\alpha_1\{\theta(u, y), y\},$$

for every (u, y) in some neighborhood of $\{\alpha(a, b), b\}$.

Let $\psi(u, y)$ be $\beta\{\theta(u, y), y\}$, and let $\phi(u)$ be $\beta\{\theta(u, b), b\}$. Then, for every (u, y) in some neighborhood of $\{\alpha(a, b), b\}$,

$$\psi_2(u, y) = \beta_1\{\theta(u, y), y\} \cdot \theta_2(u, y) + \beta_2\{\theta(u, y), y\}$$

$$= \begin{vmatrix} \alpha_1(x, y) & \alpha_2(x, y) \\ \beta_1(x, y) & \beta_2(x, y) \end{vmatrix} \cdot \alpha_1(x, y)^{-1} \quad \text{where } x = \theta(u, y)$$

$$= 0.$$

Therefore $\psi(u, y) = \psi(u, b)$ for every such (u, y); that is,

$$\beta\{\theta(u, y), y\} = \phi(u)$$

for every such (u, y); that is,

$$\beta(x, y) = \phi\{\alpha(x, y)\}$$

for every (x, y) in some neighborhood of (a, b).

Functions Restricted in Domain

1.

When we allow ourselves to consider functions restricted in domain we must be careful about certain details. One place where care is needed is in the well-known theorem that if $\phi'(x) = 0$ for every x then ϕ is constant. The proof is as follows. For any x,

$$\phi(x) = \phi(0) + x \cdot \phi'(t) \text{ for some } t \text{ between } 0 \text{ and } x$$
$$= \phi(0).$$

If, however, the domain of ϕ is restricted, we can have $\phi'(x) = 0$ for every x in the domain of ϕ without ϕ being constant. For example,

$$\phi(x) = \begin{cases} 1 & \text{if } x > 0 \\ -1 & \text{if } x < 0. \end{cases}$$

134

Then $\phi(x)$ is defined if (and only if) $x \neq 0$. $\phi'(x) = 0$ whenever $x \neq 0$, but ϕ is *not* constant.

Here the restriction, so to speak, "interrupts" the domain of the function. There is a number which is not in the domain (namely 0) but which is between two numbers which are in the domain (1 and -1, for instance). When this does *not* happen, the domain is said to be "convex" (the word will seem more apt when we consider binary functions). A typical convex domain is the set of all numbers between 0 and 1, or between -1 and 1, or between any two given numbers. For a function with such a domain the theorem is true and the proof above holds.

2.

The same ideas apply to binary functions. First let us define a set of points to be *convex* if every point which is on a line-segment joining two points of the set is in the set. For example, the set of points inside quadrilateral (i) is convex; the set of points inside quadrilateral (ii) is not, because the line-segment AB is not wholly inside the quadrilateral. A bi-convex (or plano-convex) lens is geometrically convex; a bi-concave or plano-concave lens is not.

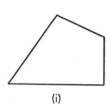

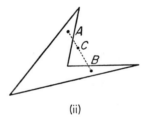

(i)   (ii)

Now we can define a set of number-pairs to be convex if the set of points which have them for cartesian coordinates is convex. For example, the set of all (x, y) for which $x > 0$ and $y > 0$ is convex, because the set of points with such coordinates is precisely the set of points in the first quadrant, and this is convex.

3.

Problems. Which of the following sets of pairs of numbers are convex?

(i) The set of all (x, y) for which $x^2 + y^2 < 1$,

(ii) The set of all (x, y) for which $x^2 + y^2 > 1$,

(iii) The set of all (x, y) for which $x^2 + y^2 \leqslant 1$,

(iv) The set of all (x, y) for which $|y| < 1$,

(v) The set of all $(x, y$ for which $x - y + 1 = 0$,

(vi) The set of all (x, y) for which $y^2 = x$.

4.

If the domain of a binary function ϕ is a convex set of pairs, and if $\phi_1(x, y) = 0$ whenever (x, y) is in that domain, then $\phi(x, y)$ is independent of x. The usual proof still applies. As a matter of fact, with most functions

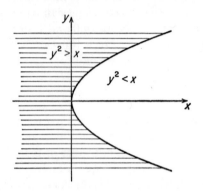

that occur naturally, the result still holds even if the domain is not convex, but we cannot rely on this, as the following example shows.

$$\phi(x, y) = \begin{cases} 0 & \text{if} \quad x < 0 \\ x^2 & \text{if} \quad x \geqslant 0 \quad \text{and} \quad y > x^{1/2} \\ -x^2 & \text{if} \quad x \geqslant 0 \quad \text{and} \quad y < -x^{1/2}. \end{cases}$$

The domain of ϕ is the "outside" of the parabola $y^2 = x$. $\phi_2(x, y) = 0$, for every (x, y) in the domain. But $\phi(x, y)$ is not independent of y, because, for instance, $\phi(1, 2) = 1$, whereas $\phi(1, -2) = -1$.

To make the graph of this function out of aluminum foil, we cut away the "inside" of the parabola, put a thumb on the origin, bend the farther "horn" upwards, so that its profile is a parabola; and bend the nearer horn similarly downward.

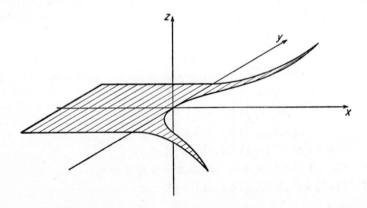

5.

Now let us consider the well-known equation of Euler:

$$u \cdot \phi_1(u, v) + v \cdot \phi_2(u, v) = 0.$$

Let us assume, not that it is universally true, but that it is true in a convex set; that is, that R is a convex set of number-pairs, and we require to find all functions ϕ which obey the chain-rule and which satisfy

(i) $\qquad u \cdot \phi_1(u, v) + v \cdot \phi_2(u, v) = 0$ whenever (u, v) is in R.

Now if $(0, 0)$ is inside R—"inside" means "in and not on the boundary of"—the solution is the same as in **L5** (vi) (namely, ϕ is constant) and the proof is the same. Let us write the proof out, so that we can see where it breaks down when $(0, 0)$ is not inside R. Given any (x, y) inside R, let

$$\psi(t) = \phi(x \cdot t, y \cdot t)$$

whenever $(x \cdot t, y \cdot t)$ is in R. Then (using the chain-rule),

$$t \cdot \psi'(t) = t \cdot x \cdot \phi_1(x \cdot t, y \cdot t) + t \cdot y \cdot \phi_2(x \cdot t, y \cdot t).$$

$(x \cdot t, y \cdot t)$ is between $(0, 0)$ and (x, y) whenever $0 < t < 1$ and is, therefore, in R. Because $(0, 0)$ is *inside* R, there is some positive d such that $(x \cdot t, y \cdot t)$ is in R whenever $-d < t < 1$. Then $\psi'(t) = 0$ whenever $-d < t < 1$ and $t \neq 0$.

Then, $\lim_{x \to 0} \psi'(x) = 0$, and so (because ψ is continuous), $\psi'(0) = 0$. Thus ψ is constant, and so $\psi(1) = \psi(0)$. That is, $\phi(x, y) = \phi(0, 0)$.

This holds for every (x, y) inside R. Because ϕ is continuous it will also hold for any (x, y) on the boundary of R. If $(0, 0)$ is not in R, this proof breaks down at the point where we prove that $t \cdot \psi'(t) = 0$, whenever $0 < t < 1$: it will be some other range of values of t for which this equation holds. But because R is convex the range will be convex, and it clearly will not contain 0, and will contain 1. Then $\psi'(t) = 0$ for every t in this range, and so $\psi(t) = \psi(1)$ for every t in this range. That is, $\phi(x \cdot t, y \cdot t) = \phi(x, y)$ for every t in this range. In other words, if ϕ is a solution of (i) obeying the chain-rule, then

(ii) $\qquad\qquad\qquad \phi(x, y) = \phi(x \cdot t, y \cdot t)$

if (x, y) is any point inside R, whenever $(x \cdot t, y \cdot t)$ is in R.

A function ϕ satisfying (ii) is "homogeneous of degree 0 in R." It is easy to prove that a function satisfying (ii) and obeying the chain-rule is a solution of (i), and now we have found the most general solution of (i) which obeys the chain-rule.

P

Greatest and Least Values of Continuous Functions

1.

We had, in Part I, a method for finding local maxima and minima. In practical problems, it is often greatest values rather than local maxima which we want. Of course, a greatest value is often a local maximum, and so the method is useful. But we are left with the problem of proving that a local maximum is, in fact, a greatest value.

Let us consider a simple example. Let us suppose that ϕ is defined by

$$\phi(x) = (1 - x^2)^{3/2}$$

whenever $-1 \leqslant x \leqslant 1$. The function is continuous (except at -1 and 1) and its domain is very restricted, so common sense suggests that it will, therefore, have a greatest value. Obviously this will not occur where $x = -1$ or $x = 1$, but somewhere in between. Now we can easily prove that there is one and only one local maximum: it will occur where $x = 0$. *If* common sense is correct and there is a greatest value, then the local maximum which we have found must be it, and so our problem is solved. As it happens, common sense *is* correct, but things are not quite as simple as they seem. Let us look into the details.

DEFINITIONS.

$[a, b]$ is the set of all x for which $a \leqslant x \leqslant b$

$<a, b>$ is the set of all x for which $a < x < b$.*

That is, $[a, b]$ consists of all numbers from a to b inclusive: it is called a *closed interval*. $<a, b>$ is an *open interval*.

Now our common-sense suggestion can be stated as follows:

(i) If ϕ is continuous in $[a, b]$, then ϕ has a greatest value in that interval. (That is, there is a u in $[a, b]$, such that $\phi(u) \geqslant \phi(x)$ whenever x is in $[a, b]$.)

This is true, and proofs can be found in many textbooks.† However, let us notice carefully that no such theorem is true for *open* intervals, as an easy example shows: If $\phi(x) = x$, then ϕ is continuous in $<0, 1>$, but has no greatest value in the interval. (Whatever u we take, there is an x in $<0, 1>$ for which $u \not\geqslant x$; for example, we could take $\frac{1}{2}(u + 1)$ for x.)

So much is revision: Now let us turn to binary functions. We require a result corresponding to (i).

2.

We make the obvious definition of closed interval for pairs of numbers: $[(a, b), (c, d)]$ is the set of all pairs (x, y) for which $a \leqslant x \leqslant c$ and $b \leqslant y \leqslant d$. Diagrammatically, it will be represented by the shaded rectangle. $|c - a, d - b|$ is its *diameter*. It can be divided into four quarters,

$$[(a, b), \{\tfrac{1}{2}(a + c), \tfrac{1}{2}(b + d)\}]$$

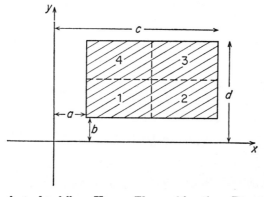

---

* This usage of $<a, b>$ follows Knopp, *Theory of functions*, Dover, 1945.

† For example, in H. A. Thurston, *Differentiation and Integration*, Blackie, 1961, p. 48.

and three similar ones, corresponding to the rectangles cut from the shaded rectangle by the dotted lines. Clearly, every pair in an interval is in at least one of its quarters.

3.

Given a set S of pairs of numbers and a binary function ϕ there may or may not be a number n with the property that $n \geqslant \phi(u, v)$ whenever (u, v) belongs to S. If there is, we say that ϕ is *bounded above* on S, and n is an *upper bound* of ϕ on S.

If ϕ has a maximum value on S—if there is a pair (p, q) in S such that $\phi(p, q) \geqslant \phi(u, v)$ whenever (u, v) is in S—then clearly $\phi(p, q)$ is an upper bound of ϕ on S, and so it is not surprising that the idea of upper bound is useful in investigating the existence of a maximum.

THEOREM. If S is a closed interval and ϕ is continuous at every pair belonging to S, then ϕ is bounded above on S.

Proof. Let us suppose that ϕ is *not* bounded above on S. Divide S into four quarters. ϕ cannot be bounded above on all of them, for if so, it would be bounded above on S. Select the first quarter on which ϕ is not bounded above, treat this in the same way and so on, thus getting an infinite sequence of closed intervals. Let the rth interval of the sequence be

$$[(a_r, b_r), (c_r, d_r)].$$

Clearly, $a_1, a_2, \ldots$ is an increasing sequence and $c_1, c_2, \ldots$ is a decreasing sequence, and $a_r < c_r$ for every r. It follows from the theory of infinite sequences that there is an x such that $a_r < x < c_r$ for every r. Similarly, there is a y such that $b_r < y < d_r$ for every r. Then the pair (x, y) is in every interval of the sequence.

Given the pair (x, y) there is a number k such that

(i) $$|\phi(u, v) - \phi(x, y)| < 1,$$

whenever

(ii) $$|x - u, y - v| < k,$$

because ϕ is continuous at (x, y).

Clearly if (x, y) and (u, v) are in the same closed interval of diameter less than k, then (ii) must hold. Also the diameter of each interval of our sequence is half that of the preceding one, and so there is an interval of the sequence whose diameter is less than k.

Thus, there is an interval I of the sequence such that (i) holds whenever (u, v) is in I. Then

$$\phi(u, v) < 1 + |\phi(x, y)|,$$

whenever (u, v) is in I, and so ϕ is bounded above in I, which conflicts with the fact that ϕ is *not* bounded above on any interval of the sequence. Hence, our original supposition is impossible.

4.

Theorem 3 is an important step towards the result we need: if ϕ *has* an upper bound, then there is at least a chance that there will be a *value* of ϕ which is an upper bound. And if there is, then it must be the greatest value.

THEOREM. If S is a closed interval, and if ϕ is continuous on S, then there are pairs (p, q) and (r, s) belonging to S such that $\phi(p, q) \geqslant \phi(x, y) \geqslant \phi(r, s)$, whenever (x, y) belongs to S.

Proof. Theorem 4 tells us that ϕ is bounded above on S. Let m be the *least* number k for which $k \geqslant \phi(u, v)$ for every (u, v) belonging to S.

(It is one of the properties of the system of real numbers that if there exists a k at all with this property, then there exists a least such k.)*

Let $\psi(x, y) = \{m - \phi(x, y)\}^{-1}$ whenever (x, y) belongs to S and $\phi(x, y) \neq m$. If there were *no* (p, q) in S for which $\phi(p, q) = m$, then ψ would be continuous on S, and so there would be (by theorem **3**) a positive number n such that $\psi(u, v) \leqslant n$ whenever (u, v) belongs to S.

Then $\phi(u, v) \leqslant m - (1/n)$ whenever (u, v) belongs to S, and so m cannot have been the *least* k. Thus there must be a (p, q) in S for which $\phi(p, q) = m$. Then $\phi(p, q) \geqslant \phi(x, y)$ whenever (x, y) belongs to S. That (r, s) exists is proved similarly.

5.

Now let us look again at problem A4. We had to find the least value of $4/y + 8/x + 2x \cdot y$ [let us call this $\phi(x, y)$], for positive x and y. We showed quite easily that *if* ϕ has a least value, then that value is $\phi(2, 1)$. In practice, we often know that there will be a least value; if we do, then the method of **K3** is good enough. But we can now complete the problem even if we do not know in advance that ϕ has a least value: we can use theorem **4** to *prove* that it has one.

Preliminary argument. $\phi(x, y)$ is large for small x, for small y, and for large x and y. That is, its graph (which is in the first octant), has "mountain ranges" along the axes. Also, points on the graph which are far distant from the origin will be high. Hence, we should be able to pick out a closed interval in which ϕ has values lower than it has outside. The least member of this set of values (which we know exists, by theorem **4**), will be the least value of ϕ.

* See, for instance, H. A. Thurston, *Differentiation and integration*, Blackie, 1961, p. 8.

Complete proof. Let S be the set of all (x, y) for which

$$\tfrac{1}{10} \leqslant x \leqslant 100 \quad \text{and} \quad \tfrac{1}{10} \leqslant y \leqslant 100.$$

There is a (u, v) in S such that $\phi(u, v) \leqslant \phi(x, y)$, whenever (x, y) is in S. $(2, 1)$ is in S and $\phi(2, 1) = 12$; therefore $\phi(u, v) \leqslant 12$.

If $0 < x \leqslant \tfrac{1}{10}$ and $y > 0$, then $\phi(x, y) > 8/x > 12$.
If $0 < y \leqslant \tfrac{1}{10}$ and $x > 0$, then $\phi(x, y) > 4/y > 12$.
If $x \geqslant 100$ and $y \geqslant \tfrac{1}{10}$, then $\phi(x, y) > 2x \cdot y > 12$.
If $y \geqslant 100$ and $x \geqslant \tfrac{1}{10}$, then $\phi(x, y) > 2x \cdot y > 12$.

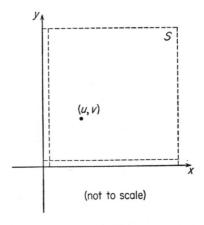

(not to scale)

Therefore if (x, y) is not inside S, and x and y are positive, then $\phi(x, y) > 12$. Hence, $\phi(x, y) \geqslant \phi(u, v)$ whether or not (x, y) is inside S, as long as x and y are positive. So $\phi(u, v)$ is the least value of ϕ. Moreover, (u, v) is not on the boundary of S (because the values of ϕ there are greater than 12), and so is *inside* S.

Then ϕ has a local minimum at (u, v); (u, v) is inside S, and therefore $\phi_1(u, v) = \phi_2(u, v) = 0$. But we have already seen that there is only one pair (u, v) inside S for which this happens, namely $(u, v) = (2, 1)$. Hence, $\phi(2, 1)$ is the least value of ϕ.

6.

Problems. Try this method on problems **K4**, **K7**, and **K12**.

7.

We might finally remark that theorem 4 is a rather special case of a more general theorem. It is possible to define much more general open and closed sets than intervals, though the same idea lies behind the definitions—diagrammatically a closed set will contain its whole "rim," and an open set will not. It then follows that a function which is continuous on a closed bounded set has a maximum and a minimum in that set. This is of great interest and importance in the more advanced theory of n-ary functions, but is substantially more difficult than our theorem 4, which is enough for our purposes.

Q

Miscellaneous Problems

1. Prove that if the result of eliminating y between $u = \phi(x, y)$, and $v = \phi(y, x)$ is $x = \psi(u, v)$, and the result of eliminating y between $u = \psi(x, y)$ and $v = \psi(y, x)$ is $x = \theta(u, v)$, then $\phi = \theta$.

2. The temperature at the point (x, y, z) is $(x^2 + y^2 + z^2)°$C. The point P moves along the curve $z = 0$, $y = x^2$, and at a certain instant is at $(2, 4, 0)$, moving at a speed 2 cm/sec in the direction of increasing x. (The coordinates are measured in cm.) Q is the point directly above P on the surface $z = 1 + \cos x$. What is the rate-of-change, at the instant in question, of the temperature of Q?

3. For each point P of the surface $z = \phi(x, y)$, P^* is defined as follows. Let N be the foot of the normal from P to $z = 0$, and N^* the reflection of N in the plane $x = y$; then P^* is the point of the surface directly over N^*. $P\dagger$ is the point of trisection of PP^* nearer to P. Assuming that ϕ has continuous derivatives, find the equation of the tangent-plane to the locus of $P\dagger$ at the point directly over $(a, 0, 0)$.

4. x, y, and u are such that $y = \phi(x, u)$. ϕ obeys the chain-rule and has the property that

$$\phi(y, v) = \phi(x, u + v)$$

whenever x, y, and u satisfy the above equation. Prove that

$$\phi_2(x, u) = \phi_2(y, v)/\phi_1(y, v),$$

whenever $\phi_1(y, v) \neq 0$ and the given equation is satisfied; and deduce that $\phi_2(x, u)$ is a function of y only. That is, prove that there is a singulary ψ such that $\phi_2(x, u) = \psi\{\phi(x, u)\}$ for every x and u.

5. Given ϕ, the variables x, y, u, and v are related by the equations $y = \phi(x, u)$, and $\phi(y, v) = \phi(x, u + v)$. Show that even if ϕ obeys the chain-rule the conclusions of 4 do not hold.

6. Solving $v = \phi(u, v, y)$ for v, substituting in $u = \psi(u, v, x)$ and solving for u gives u as a function of x and y. Find the partial derivatives of this function in terms of those of ϕ and ψ, assuming that these are differentiable.

7. Eliminating z between $u = \phi(x, y, z)$ and $v = \phi(y, z, x)$ and solving for x yields $x = \psi(u, v, y)$. Find ψ_1 and ψ_2. What, if anything, would one naturally mean by $\partial u/\partial x$, $\partial v/\partial x$ and $\partial \phi/\partial x$ in this question? (Assume that ϕ obeys the chain-rule.)

8. The gas law for a certain quantity of a certain gas is $v = \alpha(p, t)$, where α is a function which can be found by experiment. The volume of a certain balloon is given in terms of temperature and internal pressure by the formula $v = \beta(p, t)$. The balloon is filled with the gas; find the coefficient of expansion of the system in terms of α and β. (Assume that α and β obey the chain-rule.)

9. If $z = \phi(x, y)$ is solvable for x as a function of y and z, find formulas for the second-order derivatives of this function.

10. Prove that if $x = \phi(z) + \psi(y)$ is solvable for z as a function of x and y and ϕ and ψ have continuous second-order derivatives, then, in the obvious notation, $z_x \cdot z_{xy} = z_y \cdot z_{xx}$.

11. Given $u = \phi(x, y, t)$ where $t = \tau(x, y)$, write down a formula for the rate of change of u with respect to x (y being kept constant).

   A well-behaved variable varies from place to place on a flat plate and also varies with temperature. Cartesian coordinates are set up on the plate. At a certain point P the directional derivative of the variable parallel to the x-axis at a constant temperature of 15°C is 3 units; the corresponding derivative parallel to the y-axis is 2 units (each measured in the positive direction). The rate-of-change of the variable with temperature at P is -10 units.

   At a certain instant the temperature everywhere on the plate is known, and its directional derivatives at P in the positive directions of the x-axis and y-axis are, respectively, -3 and 5 units. The temperature at P is $15°$C. Find the rate-of-change of the variable with distance as one moves from P over the plate; (i) parallel to $x = 0$, in the direction of increasing y, (ii) parallel to $y = x$ in the direction of decreasing y.

12. h is a well-behaved function of x and y; new coordinates u and v are defined by $x = \frac{1}{2}\log_e (u^2 + v^2)$, $y = \arctan (v/u)$. Prove that

$$h_x^2 + h_y^2 = (u^2 + v^2)\cdot(h_u^2 + h_v^2)$$

and find a similar formula for $h_{xx} + h_{yy}$.

13. Two pairs of variables, (x, y) and (u, v) are related by $\alpha(x, y, u) = \beta(u, v, x) = 0$, where α and β are such that these equations can be solved for x and y as well-behaved functions of u and v, and vice versa. Find formulas for v_x and v_y, and prove that

$$y_u\cdot u_x + y_v\cdot v_x = 0.$$

14. A variable triangle, whose sides are of length a, b, c cm is inscribed in a fixed circle. Its angles are A, B, C, the angle A being opposite the side a, etc. Prove that if none of the angles is a right angle

$$da\cdot\sec A + db\cdot\sec B + dc\cdot\sec C = 0.$$

15. $\phi(x, y) = (x + y)\cdot\alpha(x, y)$. Prove that if α is 1-continuous at $(0, 0)$, then $\phi_1(0, 0)$ exists, even if $\alpha_1(0, 0)$ does not.

16. Find the local maxima and minima of x if $x^3 + y^3 - 3a\cdot x\cdot y = 0$, where $a > 0$.

17. Where is the flaw in the following argument? We investigate the behavior of x and y, where these variables are connected by the equation $x^3 + y^3 - 3x\cdot y = 0$. Differentiating re x, we obtain successively $x^2 + y^2\cdot y_x - y - x\cdot y_x = 0$,

(i) $\qquad 2x + 2y\cdot y_x^2 + y^2\cdot y_{xx} - 2y_x - x\cdot y_{xx} = 0$,

(ii) $\quad 2 + 2y_x^3 + 6y\cdot y_x\cdot y_{xx} + y^2\cdot y_{xxx} - 3y_{xx} - x\cdot y_{xxx} = 0.$

$(x, y) = (0, 0)$ satisfies the given equation. If a and b are the values of y_x and y_{xx} at $(0, 0)$, we get, by putting $x = y = 0$ in (i) and (ii), $-2a = 0$, and $2 + 2a^3 - 3b = 0$. This gives $a = 0$, $b = \frac{2}{3}$, that is, the derivative of y re x is zero, and the second-order derivative is positive, showing that y has a local minimum re x. Thus y must be positive for every (x, y) near to $(0, 0)$, satisfying the given equation. But if x is positive (even if it is small), $y^3 - 3y\cdot x + x^3$ changes sign as y varies from large negative values to zero. Hence, the given equation has a negative root for y which will, of course, be small if x is small. Thus y can be negative for (x, y) arbitrarily near to $(0, 0)$, satisfying the given equation.

18. Investigate the stationary values of $x^3 \cdot y^2 \cdot (6 - x - y)$.

19. Find the local maxima and minima of $x^2 + y^2$ under the condition $-2x^2 + 4x \cdot y + y^2 = 2$.

20. Find the local extrema of $a^2/x + b^2/y$, where $x + y = a$ and $b > 0$, $a \neq 0$.

21. Given the equation

(i) $$x^3 + y^3 + z^3 - 3x \cdot y \cdot z = 0,$$

show that there is a local solution $z = \phi(x, y)$ of (i) at $(1 -1, 0)$. Now, given

(ii) $$\phi(x, y) = 0,$$

show that there is a local solution of (ii) for y at $(1, -1)$.

22. Find the horizontal tangents to

$$(x^2 + y^2)^2 = 2(x^2 - y^2).$$

23. Find the horizontal and vertical tangents to

$$(x^2 + y^2 + 2x)^2 = 4(x^2 + y^2).$$

24. Prove that the coefficient of (cubical) expansion at constant pressure of a gas multiplied by the isothermal modulus of elasticity yields the rate-of-change of pressure with temperature at constant volume.

25. Variables p, v, s, t, u are such that any two may be chosen as basic, and the other three regarded as functions of them. All functions involved have continuous derivatives up to the second order, and the variables satisfy the equation $t \cdot ds = du + p \cdot dv$. We use the following notation: if $z = \phi(x, y)$, then $(z_x)_y$ denotes $\phi_1(x, y)$, and is abbreviated to z_x in any context in which it is clear that x and y are the basic variables. Prove that

$$(u_p)_v = t \cdot (s_p)_v, \quad (u_v)_p = t \cdot (s_v)_p - v, \quad (u_p)_t = t \cdot (s_p)_t - p \cdot (v_p)_t, \quad \text{and}$$
$$(u_t)_p = t \cdot (s_t)_p - p \cdot (v_t)_p.$$

Prove that, with p and t basic, $s_t \cdot h_p - s_p \cdot h_t = v \cdot s_t$, where $h = u + p \cdot v$. Find a formula, with p and t basic, for $(h_g)_s$, where $g = h - t \cdot s$.

26. The pressure in an isothermal gas varies with position, and its directional derivative parallel to the x-axis at (x, y, z) is $\delta(x, y, z)$. The internal energy is a function of pressure and volume:

$$u = \epsilon(p, v).$$

Find a formula for the directional derivative of the internal energy parallel to the x-axis.

Answers and Solutions

A2. $6c \cdot z^2$; 1; $4v$; $b \cdot a^{b-1}$; $a^a \cdot \log_e a$.

A6. (i) Let the sides be x, y, $v/x \cdot y$ cm. Given y, the area is stationary re x when $y - v/x^2 = 0$. Here the second-order derivative is positive: local minimum. There are no other extrema, and the value here is $2(2v^{1/2} \cdot y^{1/2} + v/y)$. This is least when $y = v^{1/3}$.

(ii) The area is stationary re x if and only if $y = v/x^2$; similarly re y. Thus the only stationary value is where $x = y = v^{1/3}$. By considering $x = v^{1/3} \cdot (1 + h)$, $y = v^{1/3} \cdot (1 + k)$ for small h and k we can show that this is a local minimum. Common sense then indicates that this is the least value; a strict proof will follow from **P**.

A8. (i) $x^{1/3}$; $x^{1/3}$; $-x^{1/4}$; no; $\arctan x$; $\pi + \arctan x$; $k \cdot \pi + \arctan x$; $-(1-x)^{1/4}$.

(ii) Not at $(\pm 2, 0)$.

(iii) everywhere on the graph.

B4. (i) 10; 13; 0; z^2; $x^2 - 2y \cdot z$; $v^2 + 2u \cdot w$; $2(x^2 - y^2)$; $2x \cdot z + y^2$.

(ii) $y \cdot x^{y-1}$; $x^y \cdot \log_e y$.

(iii) $-2y$; $2x$; -6; $-2u$; $-2x$.

(iv) $\{1 + a^2 \cdot (1 + a^2 - 2b^2)^{-1} \cdot (a^2 - 2b^2)^{-1/2}\} \cdot \exp \arctan$. $(a^2 - 2b^2)^{1/2}$; $(2\sqrt{2}/3) \cdot \exp \arctan \sqrt{2}$.

(v) $4/\sqrt{7}$; 0; does not exist.

B6. (i) $\theta_{11}(x, y) = \theta_{22}(x, y) = -\cos x \cdot \sin y$; $\theta_{12}(x, y) = \theta_{21}(x, y) = -\sin x \cdot \cos y$.

(ii) $3u^2 \cdot v^2$.

(iii) Work out each for a general cubic.

(iv) $-\cos x$.

C3. (i) $\frac{1}{3} - y^2$. (ii) $x^2 - \frac{1}{3}$. (iii) $x^2 - y^2$. (iv) $-4x^3/3$. (v) 0. (vi) 0. (vii) $-\frac{1}{3}$. (viii) $\phi(2, y) - \phi(1, y)$. (ix) $\cos(2 + y) - \cos(1 + y)$. (x) $3\cos 3y - 2\cos 2y$. (xi) $\phi_2(2, y) - \phi_2(1, y)$. (xii) $2\phi_1(2y, y) + \phi_2(2y, y) - \phi_1(y, y) - \phi_2(y, y)$. (xiii) $\{\beta'(y) + 1\} \cdot \cos \{\beta(y) + y\} - \{\alpha'(y) + 1\} \cdot \cos \{\alpha(y) + y\}$. (xiv) $\phi_1\{\beta(y), y\} \cdot \beta'$

$(y) + \phi_2\{\beta(y), y\} - \phi_1\{\alpha(y), y\}\cdot\alpha'(y) - \phi_2\{\alpha(y), y\}.$

(xv) $\theta\{\beta(y) + y\}\cdot\{\beta'(y) + 1\} - \theta\{\alpha(y) + y\}\cdot\{\alpha'(y) + 1\}$: use **(xiv)**.

D2. **(i)** $\theta_1(\sin x, \cos y)\cdot\cos x$; $-\theta_2(\sin y, \cos x)\cdot\sin x$.

(ii) $\lambda(x, y) = \log_e y/\log_e (x + 1)$, giving $\lambda_1(x, y) = -\log_e y/(x + 1)\cdot\log_e^2 (x + 1)$ and $\lambda_2(x, y) = 1/y\cdot\log_e (x + 1)$; $\lambda_1(\sin x, \cos y)\cdot\cos x$ and $\lambda_2 (\sin y, \cos x)\cdot\sin x$, where λ_1 and λ_2 are as before.

(iii) $\phi_1[\alpha\{y, \beta(x, y), y\}, \gamma(y, y), \delta\{y, \beta(z, y), y\}]\cdot\alpha_2\{y, \beta(x, y), y\}\cdot\beta_1(x, y); \phi_3[\alpha\{y, \beta(x, y), y\}, \gamma(y, y), \delta\{y, \beta(z, y), y\}]\cdot\delta_2\{y, \beta(z, y), y)\}\cdot\beta_1(z, y).$

(iv) $\mu(2x + y, 2y - x) = (5x^2 + 5y^2)^{1/2}$, which is easily differentiated.

D6. **(i)** $2x\cdot\alpha_1(x^2, 1/x) - \alpha_2(x^2, 1/x)/x^2$; $\cos x\cdot\alpha_1(\sin x, e^x) + e^x\cdot\alpha_2(\sin x, e^x)$; $-\alpha_1(-x, x) + \alpha_2(-x, x).$

(ii) $\psi_1(x, y) = 1/x\cdot\log_e y$; $\psi_2(x, y) = -(\log_e x)/y\cdot\log_e^2 y$; $(\cos x)/2\sin x\cdot\log_e x - (\log_e \sin x)/2x\cdot\log_e^2 x.$

(iii) $\psi_1(u, v) = -\alpha(u)$; $\psi_2(u, v) = \alpha(v)$; $\phi'(x) = -2x\cdot\alpha(x^2) + 3x^2\cdot\alpha(x^3).$

(iv) $-\sin x\cdot\gamma_1(\cos x, \sin x, x) + \cos x\cdot\gamma_2(\cos x, \sin x, x) + \gamma_3(\cos x, \sin x, x).$

(v) $0.$

(vi) 50 cm³/sec.

D8. **(i)** $4(x - y)\cdot t$, or $8t^3$.

(ii) $11635\pi/72$ cm³/sec.

(iii) $\pi\cdot r\cdot(a\cdot r + 2h\cdot b)/3$ cm³/sec.

(iv) The rate-of-change of volume is $\pi\cdot r\cdot(r - 2h)/3$ cm³/sec. $r - 2h$ decreases, and so the rate changes from positive to negative when $r:h = 2:1$.

(v) $16e + 56$ (approximately 99.4) cm³/sec and cm²/sec respectively.

(vi) Discharge at 562 units/sec.　　**(vii)** 467.6 cm³/sec.

(viii) $(15 - \pi)/750\sqrt{5}$ (approximately 0.0071) units/sec.

D14. **(i)** r^2; $\phi_1(x, y, z) = 2x$, etc.; $\psi_1(r, s, t) = 2r, \psi_2(r, s, t) = \psi_3(r, s, t) = 0.$

(ii) $r\cdot(\cos t + \sin t)\cdot\psi_1(r, t) + (\cos t - \sin t)\cdot\psi_2(r, t) = 0.$

(iii) $r_x = x/r$(or $\cos t$, or $x/(x^2 + y^2)^{1/2}$); $r_y = y/r$; $t_x = -y/r^2$; $t_y = x/r^2$; $x_r = \cos t$; $y_r = \sin t$; $x_t = -r\cdot\sin t$; $y_t = \cos t.$

(iv) $r_x = x/r$;　$r_y = y/r$;　$r_z = z/r$;　$s_x = y/(x^2 + y^2)$;　$s_y = -x/(x^2 + y^2)$;　$s_z = 0$;　$t_x = -\sin s$;　$t_y = -\cos s$;　$t_z = \cos t/r$; the others are obvious.

(v) $x_u = x_v = 1$;　$y_u = y_v = -y/x$;　$u_x = 1 - y$;　$u_y = -x$;　$v_x = v_y = x.$

(vi) $x_u = x_v = x_w = 1$; $y_u = y_v = (1 - y)/x$; $y_w = -y/x$; $z_u = (1 - z)/x \cdot y$; $z_v = -z/x \cdot y$; $z_w = 0$; $u_x = y \cdot z$ etc.; $v_x = y - y \cdot z$; $v_y = x - x \cdot z$; $v_z = -x \cdot y$; $w_x = 1 - y$; $w_y = -x$; $w_z = 0$.

(vii) From $h_u = h_x \cdot x_u + h_y \cdot y_u$; $h_x + h_y \cdot (1 - y)/x + h_z \cdot (1 - z)/x \cdot y$.

D19. (i) $\alpha\{\beta(x, y), \gamma(x)\} \cdot \beta_1(x, y) + \alpha_2\{\beta(x, y), \gamma(x)\} \cdot \gamma'(x)$;
$\alpha_1\{\beta(x, y), \gamma(x)\} \cdot \beta_2(x, y)$.

(ii) $w_x = w_u \cdot u_x + w_v \cdot v_x$; $w_y = w_u \cdot u_y$.

(iii) $\alpha_1\{x, \beta(x, y), \gamma(x, z)\} + \alpha_2\{x, \beta(x, y), \gamma(x, z)\} \cdot \beta_1(x, y) +$
$\alpha_3\{x, \beta(x, y), \gamma(x, z)\} \cdot \gamma_1(x, z)$; $\alpha_2\{x, \beta(x, y), \gamma(x, z)\} \cdot \beta_2(x, y)$;
$\alpha_3\{x, \beta(x, y), \gamma(x, z)\} \cdot \gamma_2(x, z)$.

(iv) $w_x^* = w_x + w_u \cdot u_x + w_v \cdot v_x$; $w_y^* = w_u \cdot u_y$; $w_z^* = w_v \cdot v_z$.

(v) $\eta(y, z) = \alpha\{\xi(y, z), y, z\}$ for every y and z. Differentiating re y, we get $u_y^* = u_x \cdot x_y^* + u_y$. Solving this and three similar equations, we get
$u_y^* = (u_x \cdot x_y + u_y)/(1 - u_x \cdot x_u)$; $x_y^* = (x_u \cdot u_y + x_y)/(1 - x_u \cdot u_x)$;
$u_z^* = (u_x \cdot x_z + u_z)/(1 - u_x \cdot x_u)$; $x_z^* = (x_u \cdot u_z + x_z)/(1 - x_u \cdot u_x)$.
$u_y^* = x \cdot e^y/(1 + e^{u+y+z})$; $x_y^* = -x \cdot e^{u+y+z}/(1 + e^{u+y+z})$;
$u_z^* = (1 - e^{u+y+z})/(1 + e^{u+y+z})$; $x_z^* = -2e^{y+z}/(1 + e^{u+y+z})$.

(vi) $w_y^* = w_y + w_u \cdot u_y + w_v \cdot v_u \cdot u_y$; $w_y^\dagger = w_x \cdot x_y + w_y + w_v \cdot v_x \cdot x_y$.

D21. (i) -1.   (ii) $(0, 0)$ and $(2^{2/3}, 2^{1/3})$.   (iii) $y = 1$, $y = 5^{-1/3}$.   (iv) No.

E5. (i) $4x - 7y - z + 5 = 0$.   (ii) $2x - 2y - z = 0$.   (iii) $2x - y + z + 3 = 0$.

(iv) If Q is (a, b, c) and P is $\{u, v, \phi(u, v)\}$, the derivatives re u and v of $(u - a)^2 + (v - b)^2 + \{\phi(u, v) - c\}^2$ are zero, whence $(u - a)/\phi_1(u, v) = (v - b)/\phi_2(u, v) = c - \phi(u, v)$. Then (a, b, c) satisfies the equation of the normal. The cases $\phi_1(u, v) = 0$ and $\phi_2(u, v) = 0$ are easily covered separately.

F2. (i) $\cos 1$; $-\sqrt{2} \cos 1$; $\cos (a + b) + (a + b) \cdot \cos (a - b)$.

(ii) $10 \cos t + 12 \sin t$; $t = \arctan (\frac{6}{5})$.

(iii) $-\arctan (\frac{1}{12}) < t < \pi - \arctan (\frac{1}{12})$; $t = -\arctan (\frac{1}{12})$ or $\pi - \arctan (\frac{1}{12})$.

(iv) If $\phi_1(a, b) \cdot \cos t + \phi_2(a, b) \cdot \sin t \geq 0$ for every t, then $\phi_1(a, b) = \phi_2(a, b) = 0$. Then $a = b = 0$.

(v) $\arctan (1 + \sqrt{3})/2\sqrt{2}$ upwards.

F8. (i) $(-4, -2)$.   (ii) If the given curve coincides near (a, b) with $y = \psi(x)$, then $\phi_1(a, b) + \phi_2(a, b) \cdot \psi'(a) = 0$. The curve has slope $\psi'(a)$ at a; the direction of the gradient is $\phi_1(a, b) : \phi_2(a, b)$.

(iii) $(\frac{3}{5}, \frac{4}{5})$; $\arctan 36000$.   (iv) $(2, 2, 8)$.   (v) The greatest rate-of-change of temperature with distance is the magnitude of the gradient, so the greatest rate of decrease with time is $6\sqrt{6}v$ °C/sec. The direction is $(-10/6\sqrt{6},\ -4/6\sqrt{6},\ -10/6\sqrt{6})$.

G5. (i) $(5 - \sqrt{3})$ °C/km; $2(\sqrt{3} - 1)$ °C per km.

(ii) $\cos t \cdot \exp(r \cdot \sin t) \cdot (1 + r \cdot \sin t) - 2r \cdot \sin t \cdot \cos t$.

(iii) $r \cdot \{(r \cdot \sin^2 t - \cos t) \cdot \exp(1 + r \cdot \cos t) +$ $\cos t + r \cdot (\cos^2 t - \sin^2 t)\}$.

(iv) $5/2\sqrt{2} - \sqrt{(3/2)}$; $(1 - \sqrt{3})/\sqrt{2}$.

G7. (i) $h_{rr} \cdot \cos^2 t - r^{-1} \cdot (h_{rt} + h_{tr}) \cdot \cos t \cdot \sin t - r^{-2} \cdot h_{tt} \cdot \sin^2 t +$ $r^{-1} \cdot h_r \cdot \sin^2 t + 2r^{-2} \cdot h_t \cdot \sin t \cdot \cos t$.

(ii) $h_{rr} + h_{tt}/r^2 + h_r/r$.

(iii) $\theta_{12}(p, q) + \theta_{22}(p, q) = 0$ for every p and q.

(iv) β, where $\beta(r, s, t) = r^2 \cdot \sin^2 s \cdot \cos^2 t - 2r \cdot \sin s \cdot \sin t +$ $r^2 \cdot \cos s \cdot \sin s \cdot \sin t$.

(v) $h_{pp} + h_{tt}/p^2 + h_p/p + h_{zz} = 0$. (Use (ii) with p for r).

(vi) $h_{rr} + (h_{ss} + h_{tt} \cdot \csc^2 s + h_s \cdot \cot s)/r^2 + 2h_r/r$. (Use (ii) to replace $h_{pp} + h_{zz}$ in (v) where $p = r \cdot \sin s$).

G9. $-v \cdot \sin a \cdot \tan a$; $v \cdot \tan^2 a$; $-2v \cdot \tan a$; $w \cdot (3 + \cos a)/v \cdot \sin a$.

H3. (i) $-\frac{1}{3}, 3, 1; \frac{3}{2}, -\frac{1}{3}, 2$.

(ii) The second; the second. $\phi(l, m, n) = e^l - m - n$, $\lambda(m, n) = \log_e(m + n)$ if $m + n > 0$, $\lambda(m, n) = 0$ if $m + n \leqslant 0$ shows that this first statement does not suffice.

(iii) $l_m = -m/l$, etc.

(iv) $t_p = p_t^{-1} = (v - b)/r; v_p = p_v^{-1} = v^3 \cdot (v - b)/(a \cdot v - 2a \cdot b - v^3 \cdot p)$; $t_v = v_t^{-1} = (2a \cdot b - a \cdot v + v^3 \cdot p)/r \cdot v^3$.

(v) $z_x = x_z^{-1} = -(z + 3x^2 \cdot y)/(x + 3y^5 \cdot z^2)$; $x_y = y_x^{-1}$ $= (x^3 + 5y^4 \cdot z^3)/(3x^2 \cdot y + z)$; $y_z = z_y^{-1}$ $= -(x + 3y^5 \cdot z^3)/(x^3 + 5y^4 \cdot z^3)$.

(vi) $1; \frac{3}{7}$.

(vii) $\xi\{\eta(z, x), z\} = 0$ for every x and z; differentiate re x and z.

(viii) Use (vii).

(ix) $-(3x^2 + 2x \cdot y)/(x^2 + 5y^4)$ whenever $y = \eta(x)$.

(x) $-\phi_1\{x, \eta(x)\}/\phi_2\{x, \eta(x)\}$.

H5. (i) The first two are 3(vii) and (viii). Then $u_v \cdot v_w \cdot w_x \cdot x_u = -u_w \cdot w_x \cdot x_u$, etc. (ii) Use induction.

H8. (i) $\{6(y - x) \cdot x + 2\}/3y$.

(ii) $\{\alpha_1(x, y) \cdot \beta_2(x, y) - \alpha_2(x, y) \cdot \beta_1(x, y)\}/\{\beta_2(x, y) - \alpha_2(x, y)\}$.

(iii) $\frac{5}{4}$.

(iv) $[\alpha_1\{t,\ \gamma(t)\}\cdot\beta_2\{t,\ \gamma(t)\}\ -\ \alpha_2\{t,\ \gamma(t)\}\cdot\beta_1\{t,\ \gamma(t)\}]/[\beta_2\{t,\ \gamma(t)\}\ -\ \alpha_2\{t,\ \gamma(t)\}]$.

H11. (i) $c_p = p\cdot v/t - \tfrac{1}{2}c\cdot p^2/v\cdot t^{1/2};\ c_v = (\tfrac{5}{2})c\cdot p^2/v\cdot t^{1/2}$.

(ii) Here $\phi(t) = \kappa(v,\ t) - \kappa(b,\ d) + \int_{x=b}^{v} (x^2/k)\cdot dx$ where $(a,\ b,\ d)$ is the original state. The specific heat is $p\cdot v/3t + 3c\cdot p^2/2v\cdot t^{1/2}$.
(iii) They are given by **10**(i), where $\beta_1(t,\ p) = v\cdot(p\cdot v^2 + a)\cdot(v - b)/t\cdot(p\cdot v^3 - a\cdot v + 2a\cdot b)$.

H14. $\kappa_1(v,\ t) = 0$. Then $c_p - c_v = p\cdot\beta_1(t,\ p) = r$.

I5. (i) $h - 2k + h^2 + h\cdot k + k^2; h - 2k; 0.00080109; 0.0008$.
(ii) $100(12.5 + 41 + 6.3)/(125^2 + 41^2 + 63^2)$, about $\tfrac{1}{3}$.
(iii) about -1. (*N.B.* $\Delta a = \pi/180$).

I12. (i) $dy{:}dx = -\phi_1(x,\ y) : \phi_2(x,\ y)$.
(ii) Vertical at $(2,\ 1)$. Vertical at $\pm(6,\ 9)/\sqrt{13}$. None. If $a \neq 0$ and $a\cdot b \neq h^2$, there are two horizontal tangents if $a\cdot(a\cdot f^2 + b\cdot g^2 + c\cdot h^2 - a\cdot b\cdot c - 2f\cdot g\cdot h) > 0$, none otherwise; if $a \neq 0$ and $a\cdot b = h^2$ there is one if $a\cdot f \neq g\cdot h$, none otherwise; if $a = 0$ either there are no horizontal tangents or part of the graph is a horizontal line. Horizontal at $\{-(m + \tfrac{1}{4})\pi,\ (m + \tfrac{1}{4})\pi\}$ and vertical at $\{(m + \tfrac{1}{4})\pi,\ -(m + \tfrac{1}{4})\pi\}$ for every integer m.

I15. (i) $dr\cdot\cos t - dt\cdot r\cdot\sin t;\ dr\cdot\sin t + dt\cdot r\cdot\cos t$.
(ii) $(x\cdot dx + y\cdot dy)/(x^2 + y^2)^{1/2};\ (x\cdot dy - y\cdot dx)/(x^2 + y^2)$.
(iii) $dr = dx\cdot\cos t + dy\cdot\sin t$ and $r\cdot dt - dx\cdot\sin t + dy\cdot\cos t$, by **(ii)**: these satisfy **(i)**.
(iv) $du = \phi_1(t^2,\ \sin t)\cdot d(t^2) + \phi_2(t^2,\ \sin t)\cdot d(\sin t)$.

I18. (i) $du = u_x\cdot dx$; dv similar.
(ii) $dx = \sin s\cdot\cos t\cdot dr + r\cdot\cos s\cdot\cos t\cdot ds - r\cdot\sin s\cdot\sin t\cdot dt$,
$dy = \sin s\cdot\sin t\cdot dr + r\cdot\cos s\cdot\sin t\cdot ds + r\cdot\sin s\cdot\cos t\cdot dt$,
$dz = \cos s\cdot dr - r\cdot\sin s\cdot ds$,
$dr = (x\cdot dx + y\cdot dy + z\cdot dz)/(x^2 + y^2 + z^2)^{1/2}$.
$ds = \{(x\cdot dx + y\cdot dy)\cdot z - (x^2 + y^2)\cdot dz\}/z^2\cdot(x^2 + y^2)^{1/2}$,
$dt = (x\cdot dy - y\cdot dx)/(x^2 + y^2)$.

I21. (i) $\log_e u/e^u\cdot(\log_e u\cdot\log_e v - 1/u\cdot v)$.
(ii) Putting $dw = 0$ in $\sum\phi_1(u, v, w)\cdot du = 0$ gives $\phi_1(u, v, w)\cdot du + \phi_2(u, v, w)\cdot dv = 0$.
But if $u = \alpha(v, w)$ and $\phi(u, v, w) = 0$, then
$\phi_1(u, v, w)\cdot\alpha_1(v, w) + \phi_2(u, v, w) = 0$.
(iii) $du/dv = -v/u$; see **H3**(iv).
(iv) Let $p = \pi(v,\ t),\ s = \sigma(v,\ t),\ u = \phi(v,\ t)$. Then

$t \cdot \{\sigma_1(v, t) \cdot dv + \sigma_2(v, t) \cdot dt\} = \phi_1(v, t) \cdot dv + \phi_2(v, t) \cdot dt + \pi(v, t) \cdot dv.$

Then $t \cdot \sigma_1(v, t) = \phi_1(v, t) + \pi(v, t)$ and $t \cdot \sigma_2(v, t) = \phi_2(v, t)$.

Then $t \cdot \sigma_{12}(v, t) + \sigma_1(v, t) = \phi_{12}(v, t) + \pi_2(v, t)$ and $t \cdot \sigma_{21}(v, t) = \phi_{21}(v, t)$.

Thus $\sigma_1(v, t) = \pi_2(v, t)$. Similarly for the other.

I24. (i) $x^2 \cdot y - x \cdot y^2 + x^2 + y^2$ (or anything differing by a constant).
(ii) $x^4/4 + 3x^2 \cdot y^2/2 + y^4/4$. (iii) $\sin^2 x \cdot \sin (x + y)$. (iv) impossible. (v) $x^3 \cdot y^2 + x^2 \cdot y^2$ constant. (vi) $x^2/2 + x \cdot y + y^3/3$ constant. (vii) $x^2/2 + x/y$ constant. (viii) $x = 0$ or $x^2/2 + x/y$ constant.

J2. (i) $\psi(h, k) = \psi(0, 0) + h \cdot \psi_1(h \cdot t + k \cdot t) + k \cdot \psi_2(h \cdot t, k \cdot t);$
$\psi(h, k) = \psi(0, 0) + h \cdot \psi_1(0, 0) + k \cdot \psi_2(0, 0)$
$\quad + \frac{1}{2}h^2 \cdot \psi_{11}(h \cdot t, k \cdot t) + \frac{1}{2}h \cdot k \cdot \psi_{12}(h \cdot t, k \cdot t)$
$\quad + \frac{1}{2}k \cdot h \cdot \psi_{21}(h \cdot t, k \cdot t) + \frac{1}{2}k^2 \cdot \psi_{22}(h \cdot t, k \cdot t).$

(ii) $h^5 \cdot \theta_{11111}(a, b) + 5h^4 \cdot k \cdot \theta_{11112}(a, b) + 10h^3 \cdot k^2 \cdot \theta_{11122}(a, b) + $ etc. The coefficients are the same.

(iii) $(a + h) \cdot \sin (b + k) + (b + k) \cdot \cos (a + h) = a \cdot \sin b + b \cdot \cos a + h \cdot (\sin b - b \cdot \sin a) + k \cdot (a \cdot \cos b - \cos a) - \frac{1}{2}h^2 \cdot b \cdot \cos a + h \cdot k \cdot (\cos b - \sin a) - \frac{1}{2}k^2 \cdot a \cdot \sin b + (1/6)h^3 \cdot (b + k \cdot t) \cdot \sin (a + h \cdot t) - \frac{1}{2}h^2 \cdot k \cdot \cos (a + h \cdot t) - \frac{1}{2}h \cdot k^2 \cdot \sin (b + k \cdot t) - (1/6)k^3 \cdot (a + h \cdot t) \cdot \cos (b + k \cdot t).$

(iv) Use $n = 1$.
(v) Use $n = 2$, with ψ as in (iv).

K4. (i) Local minimum at $(1, 0)$; local maxima at $u \equiv v \equiv \pi/3$, local minima at $u \equiv v \equiv -\pi/3$ modulo 2π; local minimum at $a = b = 1$; none; local minimum at $u = v = 1$; local minimum at $(-1, -2, 1)$.
(ii) Two diagonally opposite vertices are at 0 and $(1, 2, 3)$ if OA, OB, OC are axes.
(iii) $x/3 + y/6 + z/3 = 1$.

K7. (i) local minimum at $(0, 0)$. (ii) local minima at $(-\pi/3, -\pi/3)$; local maxima at $(\pi/3, \pi/3)$; other stationary pairs are (π, π), all modulo 2π. (iii) local maximum at $(-\frac{1}{2}, 4)$. (iv) The minimum of $(y - 2z + 1)^2 + y^2 + z^2$ occurs when $y = -\frac{1}{6}, z = \frac{1}{3}$. Then $x = -\frac{1}{6}$.
(v) The square of the distance between $(\frac{1}{2}x, 3 - x, 1 + x)$ and $(y - 1, -y, 4 + 3y)$ is least when $x = \frac{22}{9}$ and $y = 0$. The distance required is $\sqrt{50}/3$.

K12. (i) 14 at $(4, 1)$ and $-\frac{3}{2}$ at $(3, -\frac{3}{2})$. (ii) 2 and -2. (iii) Hottest: $(-\frac{1}{2}, \pm\sqrt{3}/2)$; coldest: $(\frac{1}{2}, 0)$ (iv) None. The stationary values are

4, 16, and 36. We can have $x + y + z$ outside this range and the condition satisfied, e.g., at

$$(1000, 8, \tfrac{9000}{499}), \quad (-1000, 8, \tfrac{9000}{501}).$$

(v) $(\pm 2\sqrt{5}, 0, \pm 1/\sqrt{5})$.

L5. (i) Each side of (I) equals $a \cdot b \cdot \psi'(a \cdot x + b \cdot y)$. (ii) As in the text.
(iii) If $\phi(u, v) = \theta\{(v - u)/4, (v + u)/2\}$, the given equation becomes $\phi_1(y - 2x, y + 2x) = 0$.
(iv) If $a = b = 0$, any function. Otherwise, $\phi(x, y) = \alpha(b \cdot x + a \cdot y)$.
(v) $\phi(x, y, z) = \beta(y - x, z + x)$. (Or $\gamma(y + z, z + x)$,
$\delta(y - x, y + z)$, etc.)
(vi) ϕ is constant.

Q1.
$$x = \psi\{\phi(x, y), \phi(y, x)\} \quad \text{for every } x \text{ and } y \tag{i}$$
and
$$x = \theta\{\psi(x, y), \psi(y, x)\} \quad \text{for every } x \text{ and } y. \tag{ii}$$
By (i),
$$y = \psi\{\phi(y, x), \phi(x, y)\} \quad \text{for every } x \text{ and } y. \tag{iii}$$
By (ii),
$$\phi(x, y) = \theta[\psi\{\phi(x, y), \phi(y, x)\}, \psi\{\phi(y, x), \phi(x, y)\}]$$
$$= \theta[x, y],$$
by (i) and (iii).

2. If the velocity of Q is (u, v, w) then that of P is $(u, v, 0)$. Then $u{:}v = 1{:}4$ (because the slope of $y = x^2$ when $x = 2$ is 4) and $u^2 + v^2 = 4$. This gives u and v. Also $u{:}w = 1{:} -\sin 2$, because the slope of $z = 1 + \cos x$ when $x = 2$ is $-\sin 2$. The required rate of change in °C/sec is
$$u \cdot \phi_1(2, 4, 1 + \cos 2) + v \cdot \phi_2(2, 4, 1 + \cos 2) + w \cdot \phi_3(2, 4, 1 + \cos 2),$$
where $\phi(x, y, z) = x^2 + y^2 + z^2$; i.e., $4(18 - \sin 2 - \sin 2 \cos 2)/\sqrt{17}$.

3. $(x - a) \cdot (4p_1 - 2p_2 - q_1 + 2q_2) + y \cdot (-2p_1 + 4p_2 + 2q_1 - q_2) = 3z - 2p + q$, where $p_i = \phi_i(2a, -a)$ and $q_i = \phi_i(-a, 2a)$.

4. $\phi\{\phi(x, u), v\} = \phi(x, u + v)$ for every x, u, and v. Differentiating re u and v we get
$$\phi_1\{\phi(x, u), v\} \cdot \phi_2(x, u) = \phi_2(x, u + v) \tag{i}$$
and
$$\phi_2\{\phi(x, u), v\} = \phi_2(x, u + v).$$
Then, if $\phi_1\{\phi(x, u), v\} \neq 0$,
$$\phi_2(x, u) = \phi_2\{\phi(x, u), v\}/\phi_1\{\phi(x, u), v\}.$$
In particular,
$$\phi_2(x, u) = \phi_2\{\phi(x, u), 0\}/\phi_1\{\phi(x, u), 0\}$$

whenever $\phi_1\{\phi(x, u), 0\} \neq 0$.

Now we define ψ by

$$\psi(t) = \begin{cases} \phi_2(t, 0)/\phi_1(t, 0) & \text{whenever } \phi_1(t, 0) \neq 0 \\ 0 & \text{whenever } \phi_1(t, 0) = 0. \end{cases}$$

The required equation now obviously holds whenever $\phi_1\{\phi(x, u), 0\} \neq 0$; if $\phi_1\{\phi(x, u), 0\} = 0$ then putting $v = 0$ in (i) yields $\phi_2(x, u) = 0$, and so the equation still holds.

5. Let $\phi(p, q)$ be $p^2 + q^2$. Then $y = x^2 + u^2$ and $y^2 + v^2 = x^2 + u^2 + 2u \cdot v + v^2$. Then $\phi_2(x, u) = 2u$; $\phi_2(y, v)/\phi_1(y, v) = v/y$. But $2u = v/y$ is not a consequence of the given relations, because $x = y = v = 1$, $u = 0$ satisfies them but not $2u = v/y$. Also, eliminating x, we get $y^2 = y + 2u \cdot v$, which shows that u is not a function of y only: so neither is $\phi_2(x, u)$.

6. If θ is the function obtained,

$$\theta_1(x, y) = f_3 \cdot (g_2 - 1)/(f_1 - f_1 \cdot g_2 + f_2 \cdot g_1 - 1 + g_2) \quad \text{and}$$
$$\theta_2(x, y) = f_2 \cdot g_3/(f_1 - f_1 \cdot g_2 + f_2 \cdot g_1 - 1 + g_2),$$

where $f_i = \psi_i(u, v, x)$ and $g_i = \phi_i(u, v, y)$. (That the denominators be non-zero is a condition that the solution be possible.)

7. $\psi_1(u, v, y) = -g_2/(f_3 \cdot g_3 - f_1 \cdot g_2)$,
$\psi_2(u, v, y) = f_3/(f_3 \cdot g_3 - f_1 \cdot g_2)$,
$\psi_3(u, v, y) = (f_2 \cdot g_2 - f_3 \cdot g_1)/(f_3 \cdot g_3 - f_1 \cdot g_2)$,

where $f_i = \phi_i(x, y, z)$ and $g_i = \phi_i(y, z, x)$.

$\partial u/\partial x$ would most naturally mean $\phi_1(x, y, z)$, but if the symbol is used it is best to specify its meaning. Similar remarks apply to $\partial v/\partial x$; $\partial \phi/\partial x$ is strictly meaningless.

8. With the gas in the balloon, both relations hold, and so pressure and volume are determined by temperature: let $p = \phi(t)$ and $v = \psi(t)$. We require $\psi'(t)/v$. Now $\psi(t) = \alpha\{\phi(t), t\}$ and $\psi(t) = \beta\{\phi(t), t\}$ for every t. If we differentiate these re t we can eliminate $\phi'(t)$ and solve for $\psi'(t)$. We obtain

$$\psi'(t)/v = (a_2 \cdot b_1 - a_1 \cdot b_2)/(b_1 - a_1) \cdot a$$

where a_i denotes $\alpha_i(p, t)$ and b_i denotes $\beta_i(p, t)$.

9. $x_{zz} = -z_{xx}/z_x^3$, $x_{yz} = (z_y \cdot z_{xx} - z_x \cdot z_{xy})/z_x^3$,

$x_{yy} = (2z_x \cdot z_y \cdot z_{xy} - z_x^2 \cdot z_{yy} - z_y^2 \cdot z_{xx})/z_x^3$, in the obvious notation.

10. Differentiation re x gives $1 = \phi'(z) \cdot z_x$. Differentiation of this re x and re y gives $0 = \phi''(z) \cdot z_x^2 + \phi'(z) \cdot z_{xx}$ and $0 = \phi''(z) \cdot z_x \cdot z_y + \phi'(z) \cdot z_{xy}$. Eliminating ϕ' and ϕ'' gives the result.

11. $\phi_1(x, y, t) + \phi_3(x, y, t) \cdot \tau_1(x, y)$. 33, $15\sqrt{2}$ units/cm.

12. $(u^2 + v^2) \cdot (h_{uu} + h_{vv})$.

13. $v_x = (a_1 \cdot b_1 - a_3 \cdot b_3)/a_3 \cdot b_2, \quad v_y = a_2 \cdot b_1/a_3 \cdot b_2,$ where a_i denotes $\alpha_i(x, y, u)$ and b_i denotes $\beta_i(u, v, x)$. $y_u \cdot u_x + y_v \cdot v_x = y_x = 0$.

14. If R cm is the radius of the circle, $a = R \cdot \sin A$, etc., whence $da = R \cdot \cos A \cdot dA$. But $A + B + C = \pi$, and so $dA + dB + dC = 0$.

15. $\phi_1(0, 0) = \lim (h \cdot \alpha_1(h, 0) - 0)/h$ as $h \to 0$; the existence of this limit requires only the property postulated.

16. Local maximum at $(2^{2/3}a, 2^{1/3}a)$. At $(0, 0)$ the curve crosses itself.

17. The relation is not locally solvable for y at $(0, 0)$.

18. The stationary values occur where $x = 0$ or $y = 0$ or $(x, y) = (3, 2)$. At $(3, 2)$ the standard test shows that there is a strict local maximum. If $y = k \cdot x$ the given expression becomes $k^2 \cdot x^5 \cdot (6 - x - k \cdot x)$ which, for fixed k and small x, changes sign with x, showing that there is no local extremum at $(0, 0)$. To investigate the behavior at $(0, b)$ where $b \neq 0$, put $y = b + z$ and investigate $x^3 \cdot (b + z)^2 \cdot (6 - b - x - z)$ for (x, z) near $(0, 0)$: this clearly has no local extremum. Finally put $x = a + z$ where $a \neq 0$ and investigate $(a + z)^3 \cdot y^2 \cdot (6 - a - y - z)$ for small y and z. If $a \neq 6$, this is approximately $y^2 \cdot a^3 \cdot (6 - a)$. Thus there is a local maximum at $(a, 0)$ if $a < 0$ or $a > 6$, a local minimum if $0 < a < 6$. We can make the expression we are investigating zero by taking y zero without taking z zero; hence these two extrema are non-strict. If $a = 6$ the expression behaves like $-a^3 \cdot y^2 \cdot (y + z)$, and so there is no local extremum here.

19. At a stationary pair, $2x \cdot dx + 2y \cdot dy = 0$; at any pair satisfying the condition, $-2x \cdot dx + 4x \cdot dy + 4y \cdot dx + 2y \cdot dy = 0$. Hence, at a stationary pair satisfying the condition, $x:y = -4(x - y):4x + 2y$. Solving this together with the condition, we get $2x = y = \pm 2/\sqrt{5}$. These then, are the two stationary pairs of the given expression under the given condition. The distinction between maxima and minima may be made geometrically (we are investigating the square of the distance from the origin of a point on a hyperbola) or as follows. At the pairs in question, the condition is locally solvable for y. Treating y as a function of x and differentiating the condition twice re x we get $-2 + 4y_x + (2x + y) \cdot y_{xx} + y_x^2 = 0$. At a stationary pair, $y_x = -\frac{1}{2}$ and $2x = y$. Then $-3\frac{3}{4} + 2y \cdot y_{xx} = 0$ at such a pair. If $u = x^2 + y^2$ then $u_{xx} = 2(1 + y_x^2 + y \cdot y_{xx})$ and so at a stationary pair $u_{xx} > 0$, giving a local minimum.

20. As 19, or simply investigate $a^2/x + b^2/(a - x)$. There is a local maximum at $\{a^2/(a - b), a \cdot b/(b - a)\}$, a local minimum at $\{a^2/(a + b), a \cdot b/(a + b)\}$.

21. N5 shows that ϕ exists. Differentiating (1) re y with $\phi(x, y)$ for z, we get $y^3 + \phi(x, y)^2 \cdot \phi_2(x, y) - x \cdot \phi(x, y) - x \cdot y \cdot \phi_2(x, y) = 0$ near $(1, -1)$. Therefore $-1 + \phi_2(1, -1) = 0$, and so $\phi_2(1, -1) \neq 0$.

22. The equation yields $(x^2 + y^2 - 1) \cdot x \cdot dx + (x^2 + y^2 + 1) \cdot y \cdot dy = 0$. For horizontal slope, $x = 0$ or $x^2 + y^2 = 1$. The former yields $y = 0$: at $(0, 0)$ both derivatives are zero and the curve crosses itself. The latter yields $x^2 = \frac{3}{4}$, $y^2 = \frac{1}{4}$. Thus the horizontal tangents are $y = \pm\frac{1}{2}$. (The tangents at $(0, 0)$ are actually $x = \pm y$).

23. $y = 0$, $x = -2a$, $y = \pm 2$, $y = \pm\sqrt{3}/2$.

24. If p_t denotes the derivative of p re t when p is regarded as a function of t and v via the gas-law, and similarly for v_t and p_v; then the coefficient of expansion is v_t/v and the modulus of elasticity is the reciprocal of $-v_p/v$. Their product is $-v_t \cdot p_v$, which equals p_t, by **H4**.

25. With p and v basic, $ds = s_p \cdot dp + s_v \cdot dv$, etc. Then $du = t \cdot (s_p \cdot dp + s_v \cdot dv) - p \cdot dv$, and so

$$u_p \cdot dp + u_v \cdot dv = t \cdot s_p \cdot dp + (t \cdot s_v - p) \cdot dv.$$

This proves the first two formulas; the next two are proved similarly with p and t basic.

$$dh = (t \cdot ds - p \cdot dv) + d(p \cdot v)$$
$$= t \cdot ds + v \cdot dp = t \cdot (s_p \cdot dp + s_t \cdot dt) + v \cdot dp.$$

Therefore $h_p = t \cdot s_p + v$ and $h_t = t \cdot s_t$, whence the next result.

$$t \cdot ds + v \cdot dp = dh = (h_g)_s \cdot dg + (h_s)_g \cdot ds$$
$$= (h_g)_s \cdot (-s \cdot dt + v \cdot dp) + (h_s)_g \cdot ds.$$

Under the condition $ds = 0$, this yields

$$v \cdot dp = (h_g)_s \cdot (-s \cdot dt + v \cdot dp), \quad \text{whence } v = (h_g)_s \cdot (-s \cdot (t_p)_s + v).$$

Anyone doubtful about the validity of the last step should refer to problem **I21**(ii). Now $(t_p)_s \cdot (s_t)_p = -(s_p)_t$, whence $(t_p)_s = -s_p/s_t$. Then

$$(h_g)_s = s_t \cdot v/(v \cdot s_t - s \cdot s_p).$$

26. $\delta(x, y, z) \cdot \{\epsilon_1(p, v) + \epsilon_2(p, v) \cdot \phi_1(p, t)\}$, where p is the pressure at (x, y, z), t is the temperature, ϕ is the function which volume is of pressure and temperature according to the gas-law, and v corresponds to p and t under the law.

Index